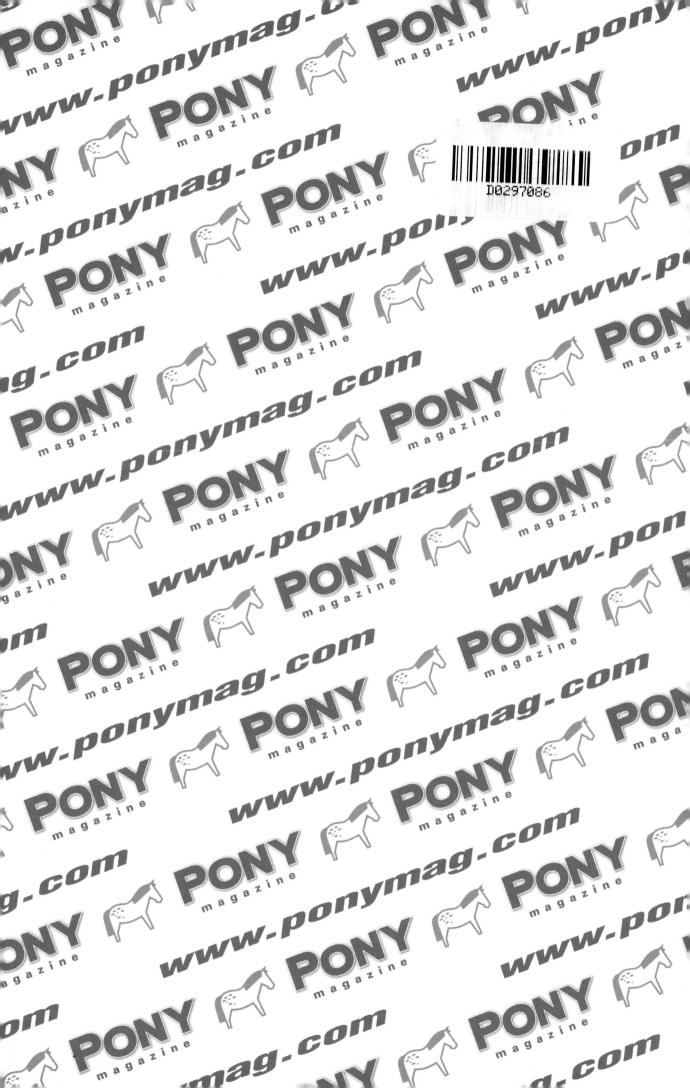

PONY: The Annual!

First published in Great Britain in 2014
DJ Murphy (Publishers) Ltd

ISBN-978-0-9928279-1-5

Who did what in **PONY: The Annual!**

Editorial Team: **Janet Rising, Laura Hodgson, Penny Rendall**
Design: **Paul Smail, Callum Cussen**
Published by: **DJ Murphy (Publishers) Ltd**, Marlborough House,
Headley Road, Grayshott, Surrey GU26 6LG

Origination by: **Suburbia Design and Communications, The Old Bank,
Berwyn Street, Llangollen LL20 8ND**
Printed by: **Graphicom via dell'Industria – 36100 Vicenza, Italy**

Photography: **DJ Murphy, Bob Atkins, Shutterstock.com**
Front cover image by **Bob Atkins**
Illustrators: **Helena Öhmark and Rebecca Enström** (26, 53, 78)

PONY Magazine is published every four weeks.
To find out more about **PONY Magazine**, visit **www.ponymag.com**

PONY™

2015

The Annual

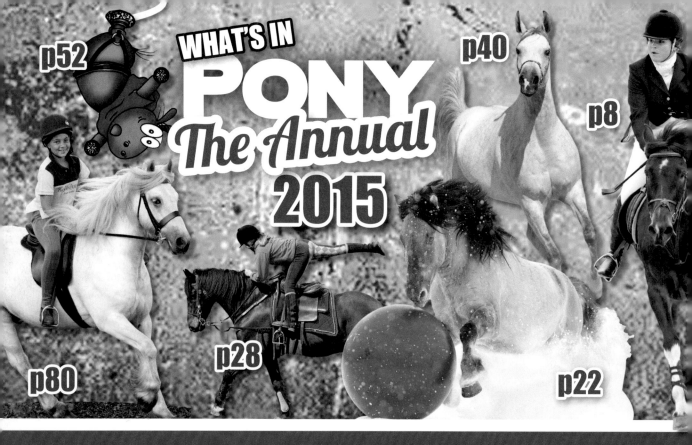

WHAT'S IN PONY The Annual 2015

p52

p40

p8

p80

p28

p22

p58

p88

p48

p74

p60

How to be a

If it's your ambition to compete at Hickstead, HOYS and Olympia, you need to get started now. Here's how!

Watch and learn

You can learn an awful lot watching other people – and you can learn what *not* to do, too! Watch how successful riders tackle a course of jumps, how they approach uprights and spreads, how they warm up, how they cope when things go wrong. Learn from their mistakes. At any top show you'll see top show jumpers watching each other's rounds and learning from them.

Book lessons

If you want to be a show jumper, you need jumping lessons! Book an instructor who specialises in jumping. They may cost more, but a few jump lessons will be of more benefit than more general lessons. Make sure you practise between each session, so you can go on to something else next time and progress quicker. All top riders have coaches and people who teach them. They know they can never stop learning.

Hurry slowly

In other words, don't overface yourself. Everyone wants to jump the big jumps, but you need to build up to this, not rush in. Just as with horses and ponies, you don't want to shatter your own confidence. So start small, concentrate on getting your jumping style and technique as good as you can, and the height of the jumps will increase without you even knowing it!

Enter shows

Clear round and minimus jumping classes may not be the big time, but it all helps to get you in a competitive frame of mind. The more competitions you enter, the more commonplace competing will seem, and the less nervous you will be. So get out there! Top show jumpers didn't start their careers at Olympia, they worked their way up the ranks!

Join The Pony Club

That way, you'll get access to great instructors and a structured competition path. Most top show jumpers started out being a member of their Pony Club team! Having a support network can help you to the top!

Competing at shows can be a dream-come-true!

Make every second count

When you're at shows don't waste time. Walk the course and decide how best to jump each jump. Watch how other competitors tackle the course so you can learn from their successes and failures. Warm up so your pony is spot on to jump. Concentrate as you jump, and give your pony every opportunity to do his best for you. Just like top show jumpers do.

Value your pony

Remember to encourage him and thank him after every round. You may be the brains behind the operation, but he's doing all the work! And remember, as the brains, you have to take responsibility when things go wrong. Don't blame your pony – think how you can make it easy for him to do better next time.

Don't waste your mistakes

Analyse every round and work out how you could have improved your score. Even if you got a clear round, there may be room for improvement. How can you jump the perfect round next time? Top riders always do this, with every round, so they get better and better.

Be jump off savvy

In the jump off? Decide where you can gain time – providing your pony is capable. A slower clear may be better than getting a fence or two down, but as you gain experience, you'll be able to cut more corners. You're in the driving seat, so you decide, then give your pony every chance of jumping clear.

Be a good sport

If you go show jumping, you'll meet the same people at each show, so be a person everyone likes. Talk with and learn from other show jumpers. Make friends. Congratulate people who do better than you, and encourage those who are still starting out. In short, be not just a good sport, but a brilliant one!

Good luck – see you at Olympia one day!

All in a day's

**What duties does a groom do every day?
We followed groom Chloe around – she
works in a private dressage yard!**

Good morning!

Chloe's day begins by feeding and
watering her charges. She has four
horses to look after. They are all stabled
at night but turned out in the day.

Making the bed

Once the horses are fed and watered, it's
time to muck out. Some of the horses are
on woodchipping beds, and some are on
straw. This means that Chloe has two muck
heaps to look after!

Wash and brush up!

It's time for morning exercise.
Chloe gives her first ride, Sandro,
a good groom before saddling up.

Taken for a ride

A hack around the forest and moorland is one of Chloe's favourite
jobs! Sandro wears a warm exercise rug to make sure he doesn't get
cold. Chloe has two more horses to exercise this morning.

...work!

Turnout time

When all the horses have been exercised, Chloe puts on their turnout rugs and turns them out in the field for some social time and some grass. But there's no time to rest just yet!

Chores, chores, chores

There are feeds for the evening to make up...

... and haynets to fill...

... and put in the hay steamer to soak, ready for evening feeds.

Then it's time for Chloe to have some lunch!

Keeping busy

In the afternoon Chloe is kept busy. One of the horses went to a show yesterday, and the trailer needs cleaning out. Chloe makes sure it is thoroughly clean, and checks the trailer to ensure everything is in good working order.

Tackle that tack!

Then it's time to clean tack. Chloe gives the tack a once-over every time it is used, and takes everything apart once a week to clean it thoroughly.

Time for bed

The horses are brought in for the night, checked over and settled with their feeds and hay. Later that evening, Chloe will skip out the beds and check on the horses again. Then it's time for bed as she has to get up early to do it all again! *Phew!*

The Voice
Natural aid
The rider's voice is vital. It can work in conjunction with other aids (saying *walk on, whoa, canter*, etc), or it can be used to calm (*steady*) and reward (*good boy!*). It works best when the words used are consistent, and upward transitions should be spoken in a brisk way, downward transitions in a more soothing manner. It can also be used to chastise – a quick growl can let the pony know he is doing something wrong, without resorting to anything more.

Hands
Natural aid
All riders should strive to achieve good hands which provide a soft yet even contact with their ponies' mouths. The inside hand asks for bend and turns. The outside hand controls the speed, bend of the neck and outside shoulder. It also asks for downward transitions.

Martingales
Artificial aid
Some people class martingales as an artificial aid. They should be fitted correctly so that they do not restrict the horse or pony, and only come into use when the horse lifts his head too high for the rider to keep control.

Spurs
Artificial aid
Spurs should only ever be worn by experienced riders to refine their leg aids. They should be used with care and consideration. It is important that spurs are fitted correctly, curved downwards, lying along the seam of the boot. They should always be blunt, without rowels.

The Aids

The aids is the name given to the rider's signals to their horse or pony. There are natural aids and artificial aids. Here is the PONY guide to aids!

The Seat
Natural aid

The rider's seat can encourage a horse or pony for more impulsion, or to slow down by the rider sitting tall, pushing the seat bones down into the saddle. Riders need to cultivate a soft, harmonious seat independent of the reins. This means the rider can stay in the correct position without relying on the reins to keep his or her balance.

Legs
Natural aid

The legs provide a comforting presence around the pony and should be close, yet supple and soft. Leg aids can encourage impulsion and ask for an upward change of pace. Closing the thighs can also slow a pony down, and the legs are used to push the pony to a resisting rein for halts and half-halts.

The inside leg asks for impulsion and for bend, and the outside leg supports the inside leg, and controls the bend of the hindquarters.

Whips
Artificial aid

A whip, used behind the rider's leg, reinforces a rider's leg aid and must be used with care and respect. It must never, ever be used in anger.

In an arena it is usual to carry a whip in the inside hand, and change to the other hand when changing the rein. It is vital when using a whip to ask a horse to go forward, that the rider allows the forward movement with the hands.

11 ways to get ponies to like you!

Everyone wants their pony to be their BFF. Here's how to do it!

1

Get inside his head

Not literally, obviously! To understand ponies you need to think like they do. That way you'll appreciate what they like to do, and what they don't enjoy. Learn all you can about ponies to give yourself a head start.

2

Reward him

Ponies love food, so you'll get plenty of Brownie points for a treat. But don't overdo it. You don't want your pony taking treats for granted and getting bargy. There are plenty of other ways to reward your pony: giving him a pat, or stroking his neck, giving him a break when riding or even loosening his girth for a moment after a gallop. It will all be appreciated.

3

Spend time with your pony

The more time you spend just hanging with your pony, the more you will learn about him, and the closer you'll become. People who just turn up and ride never really find out what their ponies love doing, and all their little quirks and personality traits. You get out what you put in – so put lots in!

4

Find out what he likes...

... and then do it! Some ponies love their ears being gently pulled, others love their shoulders scratched, or being rubbed on the forehead, or massaged. Take time to discover what your pony loves – and then spend quality time doing it!

5

Make the little things count

Like making sure his tack is clean, supple and comfortable, ensuring his bed is clean and deep for him to lie down on, changing the water in his bucket so he never has to drink stale water. Ensure your pony care is absolutely top-notch. It says you care, and that you value his comfort.

Be consistent **6**

Confident ponies have owners and riders who don't change their minds about their aids, or what they ask them, and who ensure they don't demand too much. Then they know what you want, and they don't spend their lives confused and muddled.

Ride considerately **7**

You don't have to be a brilliant rider to ride considerately. Put yourself in your pony's hooves and consider whether you ride him just a little too hard, for too long, or without proper rest. Ensure he enjoys being ridden by you – rather than dread it! You want your pony to look forward to your time together, not dive to the back of his stable when he hears your footsteps!

What not to do!

Wear perfume
Ponies hate it!

8

Loud it up

Ponies aren't ones to make a racket, and they've got big ears so keep noise to a minimum. No shouting. No roaring with laughter. No hysteria. No pop music blaring on the yard 24/7. How do you know if your pony likes *One Direction?* He may be more of a Mozart kinda pony!

Be quiet. Whisper to your pony. He'll hear you – and your relationship will be stronger.

9

Lose your temper

If your pony isn't getting what you're asking him, you need to ask in a different way. Who's the stupid one? And remember, if you do lose your temper with your pony, you can't undo it later. You'll not only knock his confidence in you, but you'll feel horrible afterwards. Don't do it!

10

Get on his nerves

11

Like us, ponies enjoy some quality time alone. Don't pester him all the time. Give him an hour to eat his lunch, or time after a ride to just chill and wind down. No-one likes a hanger-on. Time apart will only make your time together stonger as a result. Absence makes the heart grow fonder!

Part 1

GAME OF STONES

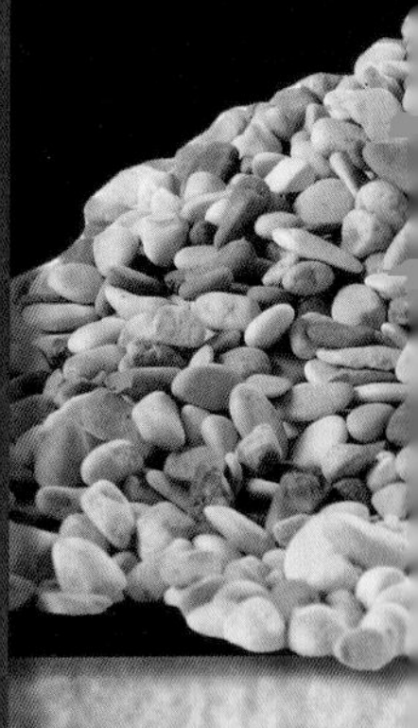

It was a quiet, nay *boring* day at PONY HQ...

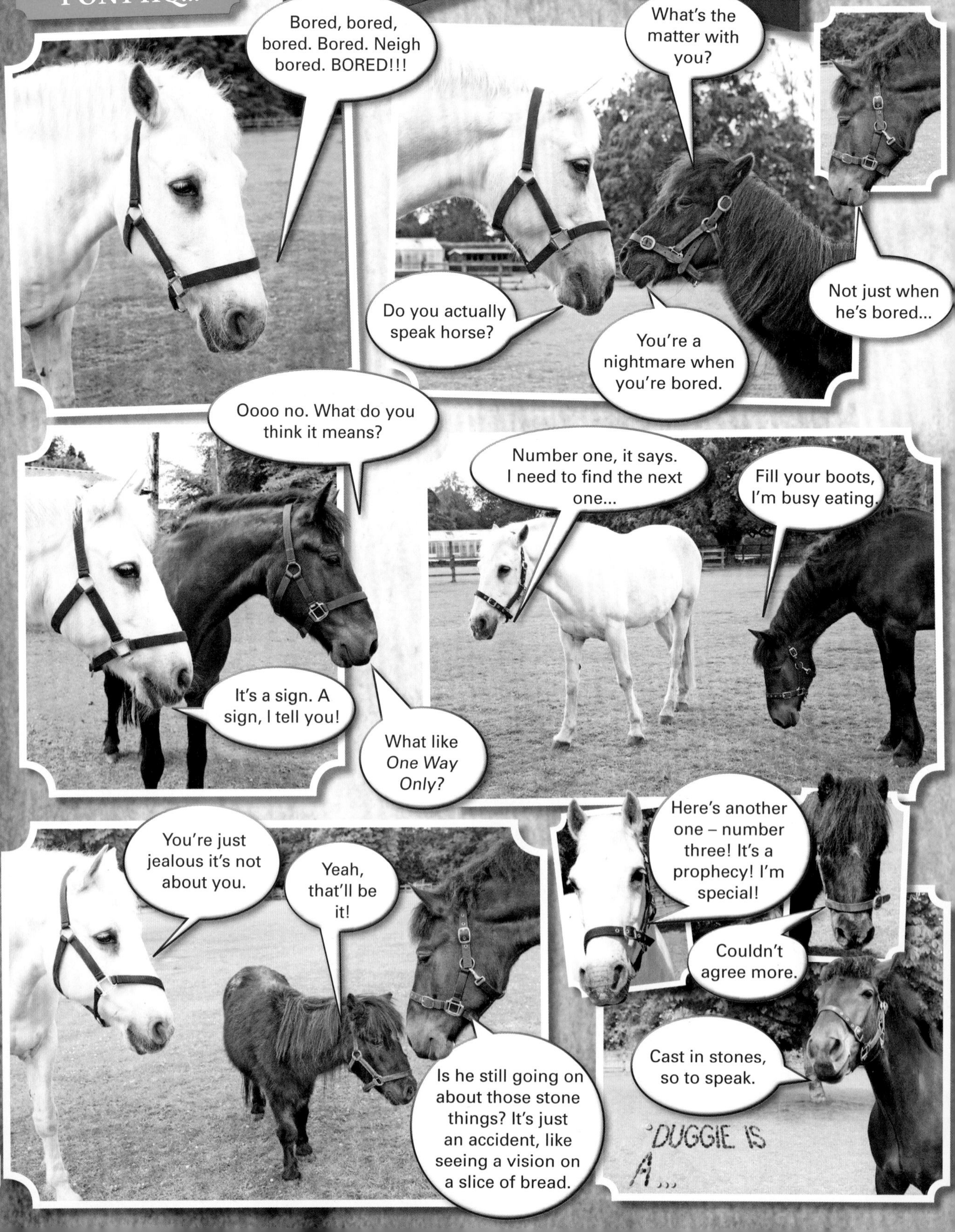

Duggie

Soloman

The Colonel

Hello, what's this? Looks like a sign. It's a sign for me...

Hey Solly, have you seen this?

What?

'DUGGIE...

Here it is! Number two. It's definitely a sign, a message. Where's three?

What do you think it is, then?

It's obvious. It's trying to tell me something.

I could tell you something...

'DUGGIE IS...

Help me look for number four.

Yes!

Is this it?

For the *special* one.

'DUGGIE IS A PONY...

What will the stones reveal? Is Duggie the chosen one? Do the stones hold a message for our hero? Turn to page 90 to find out in part two of *Game of Stones!*

And here's five. I'm the one who... what?

'DUGGIE IS A PONY WHO...

17

Welsh ponies!

There are four distinct Welsh ponies – one for every occasion and use! Although no longer wild, some Welsh ponies still run feral on the Welsh hills. They are arresting and proud ponies, beautiful and tough!

Welsh Section A – Welsh Mountain Pony

The influence of Arab breeding is obvious when you see the pretty Welsh Mountain – it has a lovely dished face and a floating action.

- Max height: 12hh
- Coat colours: Grey, chestnut and palomino are most common. They are never piebald or skewbald!
- The Welsh Pony Section A is popular all over the world!

Welsh Section B

This pony came about by crossing Welsh Mountain ponies with the Welsh cob. It is a definite riding pony type.

- Max height: 13.2hh
- They are hardy, well balanced and fast, and are popular as riding ponies.

DYK?

In 1901, the Welsh Pony and Cob Society was formed, with the stud book published the following year. It wasn't until 1949 that the four sections of the stud book (A, B, C, and D) were introduced.

Welsh Section C

This pony is a small cob. Both the Section C and Section D evolved from Welsh Mountain Ponies crossed with Spanish horses, and other horses brought over by the ancient Romans when they invaded Britain. The resulting horses, bred to Mountain Pony mares, were ridden by the English armies from the 12th Century.

- Max height 13.2hh
- Known as the Welsh Pony of Cob type
- They excel in harness and at jumping
- Colour: Any except skewbald and piebald

Welsh Section D – The Welsh Cob

These are real cob types, all-rounders which excel in harness. High-stepping, they were popular with tradesmen who liked an eye-catching horse to pull their carts, one which could deliver their wares in record time – especially useful for butchers before refrigeration!

- Max height: up to 15hh
- Colour: Any except piebald and skewbald. Black is popular and eye-catching
- Often thought of as the best ride-and-drive equine in the world!
- Often bred with Thorougbreds to produce competiton and good riding horses
- Were used by the army to pull guns and equipment.

THE HARD LIFE OF A HORSE

PONY short story winner!

By Grace Bowman

EVER WONDERED WHAT IT'S LIKE TO BE A HORSE?

COMET'S STORY

Humans are so predictable – so let me set the scene. I was in my stable at Willow Tree Livery Yard, minding my own business, when my owner, Penny, put on my halter and led me to one of the wash boxes.

Oh, no, not again! I pulled backwards on my lead rope. One look at the wash box and I knew – there was a show tomorrow!

"Let's get you cleaned up for the show tomorrow. We want you looking beautiful, don't we!"

See what I mean? The wash boxes smell funny. A bit – what's the word – oh yes, *clean*. Why clean? Why not dirty? I love dirty! I hate baths. Absolutely hate them. One minute you are dry and comfortable, the next you are wet and very, *very* uncomfortable.

The sponge was dipped into a bucket of coldness (it is supposed to be warm!), splattered with shampoo and rubbed all over my body. After all the shampoo was washed off with a hosepipe, the sweat scraper (I'm not even sweating) and the towel is drying me off. Then I stand for five minutes (boring) in my cool sweat rug (cool, but I'm still not sweating!).

Give it up now! Penny was on the fourth plait in my mane, and I was trying to tell her that there was no point in trying, I would just mess them up anyway. I *accidentally* lifted up my hoof and stamped it on to the ground.

"Owwwww!"

Oops! Maybe it didn't touch the ground, but I was trying to tell you... oh never mind.

My hoof crashed against the door. I saw my food bowl, metres away from me. It looked *sooo* yummy, too. Mouth-watering. Ahhh! Penny was standing across the yard with Matt, one of the other members of Willow Tree and a friend of Penny's. Lenny, Matt's horse, told me that Matt had a bit of a crush on Penny. We horses can tell gossip and rumours, too, you know. My tummy made a loud rumble. Penny gave me my well-deserved dinner. Finally!

"Back in a minute," she had said. After five minutes I had gobbled down my food, eaten a bit of hay, drunk some water and stuck my beautiful face over my door. I stood patiently, but my eyes said, *Hurry up, come on, chop chop. And I am late for my bedtime.* JOKE!

ICICLE'S STORY

I felt a queer feeling in the air, but I wasn't sure why. It was dusk at the stables and was neither hot, nor cold, just right, in fact. Ginger and Flicker didn't seem to notice the queerness and were playing hoofball, as they like to call it.

"Come on, girlies!" I was glad to hear my part-owner's voice and, for that matter, see him. My friends and I are owned by two people, Matt and Penny. They are always lovely! Ginger and Flicker cantered towards him and he gave them a treat before they galloped off.

"Not again!" Matt groaned. Then came the fabulous me, ears pricked, and I stopped for a cosy cuddle with them. Ahhh, how lovely!

Horses, like my two inseparable friends, Ginger and Flicker, know and use humans as a food source. I, on the other hand, like to be reassured and have a cuddle from anyone who stops at our field.

"Bedtime!" Matt called. "Come on sweeties!" I trotted steadily after him and settled in my stable. Matt watched me puff up my pillows, and laughed. "Princess!" he teased.

No matter how hard I tried, I could not sleep. The hoot of an owl was the only comfort I had. In the other stalls, Ginger and Flicker snored softly. Maybe Ginger didn't snore *softly*, but she did snore, and snore and snore! Anyway, I didn't know if it was the queer feeling or something else that was keeping me awake, I could not explain. I soon became scared, and any noise made me jumpy. I wanted to know, I had to, yet I didn't. What could it be that was making me feel so scared...?

GINGER AND FLICKER'S STORY

Finally, our turn to tell a story! Once upon a time, in a faraway land...

"Oh for sugar beet's sake...!"

"Shut up Ginger, I am trying to tell our story."

"Fine, go ahead, YAWN!"

"Ignore her! Anyway, we woke up in the morning and started our daily routines: checking hay nets, puffing up shavings and having a good stretch and shake. Our owner, Penny, came at last with feed buckets. Of course, I was the first to notice that Penny was upset...."

"No way, that was soooo me!"

"No it wasn't!"

"Yes it was!"

"Whatever! So Penny was upset – but why? She gave us both a hug, a tight one, and then gently stroked our necks. What was going on?

Ginger speaking – this is my part of the story. So far, the three of us had no idea what was happening,

> "GOODBYE MY PRECIOUS ONES, I WILL MISS YOU..."

and what was going to happen next. Little did we know our lives were going to be turned upside down. You will find out what I mean later. But suddenly, Penny came out of the store room carrying a lot of boxes. My eyesight is not the best, but on one of those boxes it clearly said RUGS AND BOOTS. We were horrified. No way! What had we done? How on earth could Penny even think of sending us away?

My turn again! We were very confused – more than confused! We were upset, but even more than upset. It was only when Penny put us into travelling gear that we understood. Now we knew for sure that we were leaving. Matt had arrived and Penny tried hard to fight back tears.

Matt whispered softly these words to us: "Goodbye my precious ones. I will miss you..." His voice was choked with emotion. I didn't want to say goodbye, no-one did, but we had to, and that was that. All three of us were lead into the main yard at Willow Tree Stables where a small horsebox was parked. The ramp was lowered and inside was as empty as my heart.

Matt and Penny loaded us. *NO!* we screamed, but they could not hear us. A strange woman was talking to Penny, laughing, unlike Penny. A river of tears exploded from her eyes. The strange woman gave her a hug and joked, "There will be a flood if you keep crying!" It didn't sound like a joke.

"Get me out of this nightmare!" Ginger cried. Nobody heard us, nobody ever does. Penny tickled our ears and swiftly moved off the horsebox. Then it started to move. We were silent. We were going.

The journey in the horsebox didn't take too long but it seemed to last forever. Flicker, Icicle and I had no idea where we were going. Suddenly we arrived, and then we decided that we didn't want the journey to end after all. Nevertheless, we were dragged off the horsebox. This wasn't home, take us back!

The strange woman called herself Amanda. So, Amanda, take us back home or I will kick you! Of course she didn't, and I didn't dare kick her. Instead, I showed my best physical threat – rearing! Amanda pulled me back down. Then we were in stables. All by ourselves. Was this the end?

COMET'S STORY

This morning, it rained. It rained and rained and rained. Everything was soggy, even the barn cat – what a soggy moggy she was. Hey, wasn't there going to be a show today? Ooops, no show today – cancelled! Yippee!

LITTLE DID WE KNOW OUR LIVES WERE GOING TO BE TURNED UPSIDE DOWN

Now this is the life of the most attractive, intelligent and attractive (did I say that before, oh never mind!) horse ever. Going out in the field (the muddiest) in the rain, what could be more fabulous than that? Don't you agree? As soon as Penny let me go I galloped, bucked and whinnied. I love the field!

Two glorious hours later, Penny came back. "Comet!" she screamed. I leapt out of my skin. What did I do? Had I a mirror, I would have seen myself and all the mud splattered on my coat. But I didn't. Penny was muttering and sighing, all the way to the wash box. NOOOOOO!

As the sun set at Willow Tree Livery Yard, I knew that tomorrow could be a good day! The sky had promised sunny weather. Maybe I could go on a hack, or back in the field, or maybe...

GINGER AND FLICKER'S STORY

We were still here, waiting. We had been let out into a vast meadow with lush grass to munch on. Icicle pined for Penny, we all did, but I decided not to think about it and get on with the holiday. When Amanda came back a few hours later to see how we had settled in, we finally found out why we were here.

"You are here to be broken-in," she said. "When you are finished, you will go back home."

Oh! We suddenly realised our mistake – poor Penny, we missed her so much. We wanted this breaking-in thing to be over so we could go back home soon!

COMET'S STORY

AS SOON AS PENNY LET ME GO I GALLOPED, BUCKED AND WHINNIED

The next morning I was loaded into the horsebox. Oh great, the show had to be today, instead, didn't it! But the journey took longer than it did when we went to a show. Finally, I smelt something familiar. Salt! What? Seagulls screeched up above. Of course, we were at the seaside!

We were at the beach for most of the day. It was amazing, cantering into the waves and across the sand – relaxing or what? The spray of the water was surprisingly warm and made me excited. Penny loved it more than I did. Or maybe not, change that! Penny loved it almost as much as I did. Today was the best!

After six months Icicle, Ginger and Flicker were fully broken. Comet was still on cloud nine after his trip to the seaside – but he still hadn't gone to that show!

Winter wonderland!

Snowfall transforms the countryside into a winter wonderland – and horses and ponies often *love* it!

LET'S GO!

Turn your pony out in a snowy field and stand back! Ponies will often gallop around in the snow, and have mock fights. They seem to get as excited about the white stuff as we do!

Plus point: Ponies stay clean in the snow! The mud is hidden and the snow cleans off any remaining dirt!

Minus point: Snow can hide ice, ruts and frozen ground, so beware if your fields are not very smooth under the whiteness. And take care when the snow freezes – it can be slippery, rutted and dangerous for your pony's legs.

STAY EATING, STAY WARM!

Ponies who are turned out all day – or all the time – will need supplementary food. With a heavy snowfall, all the grass will be hidden. Make sure you offer your pony some hay to eat. And keep feeding him after the thaw as the grass will be waterlogged, and not very nice at all.

Plus point: Hay acts as central heating for ponies. Eating hay keeps ponies warm!

Minus point: The snow will quickly make hay sodden and cold. It is better to hang hay from a haynet on a fence or tree. Make sure it is high enough, and won't trail on the ground when it is empty, which would be dangerous if your pony were to get a hoof caught.

PLAYTIME!

Snow-covered paddocks and outdoor schools are the perfect place to allow stable-kept ponies to let off some steam. A giant ball is a brilliant toy for this pony! If snow means you can't get out and ride, turning your pony out in an arena is a great way to keep him happy, instead of climbing the walls of his stable!

Plus point: Watching your pony play can be relaxing for both of you. It's a great way to get to know more about what your pony likes to do.

Minus point: The air is much colder when there is snow around – it's like standing in a giant freezer! Don't leave your pony out for too long as he may get cold or even chilled. Make sure he enjoys his time out in the snow, rather than wishing he was in a warm stable!

ROLY-POLY!

Most ponies will treat themselves to a roll in the white stuff – it must be like taking a refreshing cold shower! Be prepared if you turn your pony out, he could come in rather soggy, but happy!

Plus point: Your pony will have given himself a winter bath when he rolled. All you need to do is make sure he gets warm and dry again before you rug him up for the night.

Minus point: You may find that your pony has morphed into a walking snowpony! Ice can cling to manes, tails and fetlocks, and it can ball up inside hooves. When you bring your pony in, get all the icicles out of his mane, tail and feather, and pick out his hooves, making sure you remove the ice completely. Rug him in a wicking rug to get him dry, and check his ears to make sure he is warm enough. Now give him an extra deep bed to dry his legs and keep them warm, too.

Enjoy the snow!

MAKE! PLACEMATS AND COASTERS

- Cork tiles
- Sticky back plastic
- Scissors
- A glue stick
- Ruler
- Ballpoint pen
- Pictures of your fave pony
- Decorations (optional)

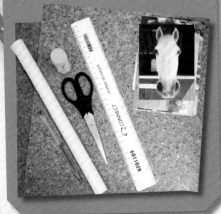

HOW TO DO IT!

STEP 1

Take a cork tile, ruler and ballpoint pen. Measure out 23cm square on your tile for a placemat, or 10cm square for a coaster, and mark the measurements with two lines.

STEP 2

Cut down the lines you have made very carefully with scissors. You should end up with a square piece of cork.

TOP TIP

Cutting slowly helps to keep the edges of the cork neat and smooth.

STEP 3

Grab your pony pics and stick them onto the cork with a glue stick. You could use one large image or create a collage of smaller ones. Add some decorations if you like (we went for gold and silver stars)!

TOP TIP

If you do add decorations, remember to keep them flat so that you don't end up with an uneven surface. It's not much fun trying to eat your dinner from a plate that's wobbling all over the place!!

STEP 4

Trim off a section of sticky back plastic from the reel, a bit bigger all around than you need.

STEP 5

Cover your placemats or coasters. Slowly roll the plastic over the placemat or coaster, smoothing out any bubbles as you go. Trim off any excess from the edges.

STEP 6

Enjoy using your fab creation!

Charlie in the FUN RUN!

Being brave

What could a runaway horse teach Kathryn?

I was shovelling manure into bags for my dad when it happened. Horses were kept at the end of our lane and I had offered, one snowy day, to bag up manure for my dad's garden, earning some extra money for my riding lessons. I had filled only one bag when I heard a sound and I looked up to see a grey horse, tacked-up and riderless, looking nervously at me.

TAKING CHARGE

I stood there for a moment or two, my mouth open, wondering what to do. I didn't recognise the horse – he didn't live in the stables. Rustling the empty chocolate wrapper in my pocket the grey pricked his ears and took a step towards me. It was easy to take hold of his reins and as soon as I did he seemed to relax, as if someone had taken charge.

Taken charge. *Me.*

I gulped and ran up his stirrups with trembling fingers as the horse stepped around me. The riding school ponies stood like rocks when I tacked them up, but this bigger, wilder-looking horse was no school pony. I knew I had to be confident – or at least act it.

> "I looked up to see a grey horse, tacked-up and riderless..."

"Horses know when you're nervous, Kathryn," my instructor Paula told me whenever she saw me duck away from a pony's nudge, or lead Rocky, who liked to step on your toes, at arm's length. I had to pretend to be confident. I had to be *in charge*. But my fingers were shaking, the horse would know I was scared. I scratched his neck and spoke to him and gradually my voice got stronger, stopped wobbling and sounded more confident than I felt.

"Good boy, there now, it's okay..." the more I said it, the more I believed it and the horse suddenly sighed and stood still. He wasn't clipped, but I wondered whether he ought to have a rug on. It was cold, but I noticed he wasn't sweating. Perhaps he would be all right without one. Perhaps I ought to walk him round. Perhaps not. *Perhaps, perhaps, perhaps....* We stood there, looking at each other, neither knowing what to do next.

FOLLOWING HOOFPRINTS

Snow. There would be hoofprints in the snow! I led the horse around the muck heap and found his prints. They led off into the distance, along the common, towards the woods. If I were to reunite him with his rider, I had to retrace his hoofprints. So we set off, the horse and I. I looked at his saddle. It would be amazing to ride him – but it was out of the question. I had no riding hat, and he had already lost his own rider. It would be madness to try. A part of me wanted to, but the sensible part made me stay on my own two feet.

The horse walked quite calmly, and we made good progress, walking silently through the wood, following the prints in the snow. I pretended this big horse was mine. Imagined turning up at the riding school on this grey gelding, imagined being brave, leaping jumps, being the envy of the other pupils who usually did better than I did. We'd hack for hours, enter shows, win dressage and jumping competitions and be best friends. He'd follow me like a dog – I wouldn't need tack, there would be such an incredible bond between us.

Then I saw the horse's owner walking towards us, her hat in her hand, dirt down one side of her jodhpurs.

REUNITED

"Oh thank goodness, you've found Dove, I was so worried!" She took the reins out of my hand and my dream melted away as Dove went from being my horse back to hers. "You naughty boy!" she scolded him, but she didn't mean it. And Dove nuzzled his owner as if to apologise for dumping her in the snow.

"Thanks so much. You must ride?" It was a question, and I nodded, reluctant to admit I rode at the riding school. "Because Dove can be funny with people who don't know horses. Lucky he ran into someone with experience. Thanks again!"

> "Horses know when you're nervous, Kathryn,"

She mounted, smiled, turned Dove and rode away and I watched them until Dove's snowy tail disappeared through the trees.

Someone with experience, she had said. Me. I walked back to filling muck sacks, knowing I would never be nervous of the riding school ponies again. I could be brave when it mattered. And it did. It mattered very much. It had mattered to Dove. And to me.

I heard a sound...

posed by model

27

What are they doing?

1 ....

2 ....

[Christopher Halloran/Shutterstock.com]

3 ....

4 ....

[Christopher Halloran/Shutterstock.com]

5 ....

6 ....

7

[ECOPrint/ss.com]

....

8 ....

9 ....

10 ....

11 ....

12 ....

Turn to page 98 to find out if you are right!

WHAT CAME FIRST, THE SADDLE OR THE BRIDLE?

Can you imagine life without saddles and bridles? Check out where they came from, and how they evolved into what we know today!

Early saddles

For many years after the domestication of horses, riders did not use saddles at all! It was bridles that were invented first to help riders control their mounts.

The first saddles appeared 4,000 years ago, as a cloth pad, which then evolved into a leather one. They offered very little support and served more as a buffer between horse and rider.

DYK...
None of these early types of saddles had stirrups.

DYK...
The cloths and early saddles became symbols of an individual's wealth and status, and were decorated and embellished with gold, wood carvings, leather and hair.

Saddles made on a frame were invented around 400-500 BC. These had two parallel cushions with an attached girth, as well as a pommel and a cantle.

Saddles with solid trees evolved from this early design. The design resembled a very simple saddle, which had a leather base with four pommels for grip.

Saddles were not used in Europe until the middle ages, as medieval knights would have found riding bareback a problem in all their armour!

Ancient saddles

Pictures – Chris Taylor

A leather cloth with four pomm

The invention of the solid tree saddle was very significant as it allowed the weight of the rider to be carried off the horse's spine. This increased the comfort of the horse and so prolonged his life, which greatly helped the owners.

Along came stirrups...

Early designs of stirrups can be traced to India, where the design consisted of a single loop for the rider to put his big toe through! As you can imagine, this was not very stable and did not help the rider to mount the horse. The invention quickly evolved as riders found that standing up made it easier to throw spears from the saddle, for hunting and warfare.

DYK...

Stirrups were first used in China, then spread to Europe.

Modern saddles

Today, the style of the saddle is well established, and there are different types available for different types of English style riding, such as general purpose, dressage and forward-cut jumping saddles. We're spoilt for choice!

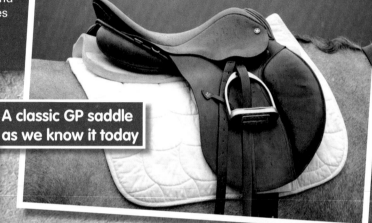

A classic GP saddle as we know it today

Early bridles

Bridles have been used since the domestication of horses, as a method of controlling the horse. When horses were first domesticated, bridles were mainly made of rope or a similar material, used in a loop around the horse's neck. These evolved into bridles with a type of noseband, but no bit.

DYK...

Before the development of bridles with bits, steering was controlled through the rider's legs!

Bits, bits, bits

Historic evidence suggests there was a type of bitless bridle used before the development of the bit. The domestication of the horse occurred between 4500 BC and 3500 BC, but the earliest evidence of bridles with bits dates to around 3500 BC–3000 BC, suggesting that bits were invented much later than the bridle. Snaffle and curb types were the first bits to evolve.

DYK...

Early bits were made from natural materials, like vines, other plant material or bone. These were later replaced by metal.

A modern horse in modern tack

Modern bridles

Bridles today are almost always made of leather, as it is hardwearing and comfortable for horses and ponies. Modern bridles come in a variety of styles, such as bitless ones – like the Hackamore – and the double bridle.

Nosebands have also developed so that there is now a noseband to suit every horse and pony, and the activities they do. Think cavessons, flashes and grackles, and the different ways in which they work!

The evolution of bridles and bits has been influenced by equestrian sports, because as the different disciplines have developed, so has the need for a wider variety of bridles and bits!

A classic modern bridle

8... 9... 10... coming,-re

Aww, hide me Mum!

Make like a flower!

I'm another leg!

We're bushy trees...

I'm a branch...

Do horses play hide-and-seek? Of course they do – and here's the proof!

Peek-a-boo!

We're inseparable!

You ain't seen me...

Where's Colonel?

...day or not!

Camouflage!

We're not here...

Try your hand out these fiendish beauties!

DISCIPLINES WORDSEARCH

Can you find all our equestrian disciplines (below) in our wordsearch?

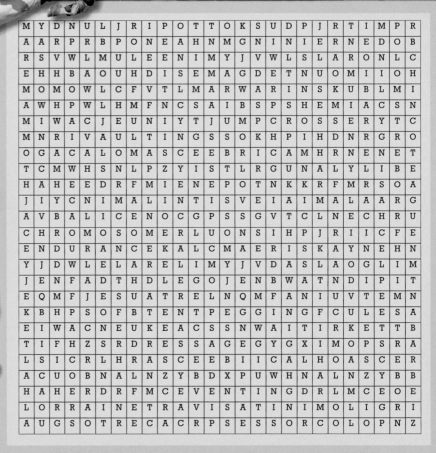

Pix: Reglan Paassen, Olaru79, Ventura/Shutterstock.com

M	Y	D	N	U	L	J	R	I	P	O	T	T	O	K	S	U	D	P	J	R	T	I	M	P	R
A	A	R	P	R	B	P	O	N	E	A	H	N	M	G	N	I	N	I	E	R	N	E	D	O	B
R	S	V	W	L	M	U	L	E	E	N	I	M	Y	J	J	V	W	L	S	L	A	R	O	N	L	C
E	H	H	B	A	O	U	H	D	I	S	E	M	A	G	D	E	T	N	U	O	M	I	I	O	H
M	O	M	O	W	L	C	F	V	T	L	M	A	R	W	A	R	I	N	S	K	U	B	L	M	I
A	W	H	P	W	L	H	M	F	N	C	S	A	I	B	S	P	S	H	E	M	I	A	C	S	N
M	I	W	A	C	J	E	U	N	I	Y	T	J	U	M	P	C	R	O	S	S	E	R	Y	T	C
M	N	R	I	V	A	U	L	T	I	N	G	S	S	O	K	H	P	I	H	D	N	R	G	R	O
O	G	A	C	A	L	O	M	A	S	C	E	E	B	R	I	C	A	M	H	R	N	E	N	E	T
T	C	M	W	H	S	N	L	P	Z	Y	I	S	T	L	R	G	U	N	A	L	Y	L	I	B	E
H	A	H	E	E	D	R	F	M	I	E	N	E	P	O	T	N	K	K	R	F	M	R	S	O	A
J	I	Y	C	N	I	M	A	L	I	N	T	I	S	V	E	I	A	I	M	A	L	A	A	R	G
A	V	B	A	L	I	C	E	N	O	C	G	P	S	S	G	V	T	C	L	N	E	C	H	R	U
C	H	R	O	M	O	S	O	M	E	R	L	U	O	N	S	I	H	P	J	R	I	I	C	F	E
E	N	D	U	R	A	N	C	E	K	A	L	C	M	A	E	R	I	S	K	A	Y	N	E	H	N
Y	J	D	W	L	E	L	A	R	E	L	I	M	Y	J	J	V	D	A	S	L	A	O	G	L	I	M
J	E	N	F	A	D	T	H	D	L	E	G	O	J	E	N	B	W	A	T	N	D	I	P	I	T
E	Q	M	F	J	E	S	U	A	T	R	E	L	N	Q	M	F	A	N	I	U	V	T	E	M	N
K	B	H	P	S	O	F	B	T	E	N	T	P	E	G	G	I	N	G	F	C	U	L	E	S	A
E	I	W	A	C	N	E	U	K	E	A	C	S	S	N	W	A	I	T	I	R	K	E	T	T	B
T	I	F	H	Z	S	R	D	R	E	S	S	A	G	E	G	Y	G	X	I	M	O	P	S	R	A
L	S	I	C	R	L	H	R	A	S	C	E	E	B	I	I	C	A	L	H	O	A	S	C	E	R
A	C	U	O	B	N	A	L	N	Z	Y	B	D	X	P	U	W	H	N	A	L	N	Z	Y	B	B
H	A	H	E	R	D	R	F	M	C	E	V	E	N	T	I	N	G	D	R	L	M	C	E	O	E
L	O	R	R	A	I	N	E	T	R	A	V	I	S	A	T	I	N	I	M	O	L	I	G	R	I
A	U	G	S	O	T	R	E	C	A	C	R	P	S	E	S	S	O	R	C	O	L	O	P	N	Z

Barrel racing	Endurance	Jumpcross	Polo	Showing	Tent pegging
Dressage	Eventing	Mounted games	Polocrosse	Show jumping	Trec
Driving	Horseball		Reining	Steeplechasing	Vaulting

ODD ONE OUT

Which is the odd one out in our collections?

1. Donkey, Ass, Mule, Jennet, Hinny, Jack, Morgan

2. Stirrups, Girth, Irons, Snaffle, Buckle guards, Numnah, Leathers

3. Exmoor, Dartmoor, Connemara, Shire, Shetland, Lundy, Highland, Fell, Dales

4. Mary King, Charlotte Dujardin, William Fox-Pitt, Oliver Townend, Piggy French, Lucinda Green, Mark Todd

5. Piebald, Pinto, Appaloosa, Skewbald, Paint, Tri-coloured, Tobiano

6. Tennessee Walker, Saddlebred, Haflinger, Morgan, Missouri Fox-trotter, Narragansett Pacer, Rocky Mountain Pony

7. Shoulder-in, Half-pass, Full-pass, Travers, Leg Yield, Renvers, Winvers

8. Sausage, Tendon, Overreach, Brushing, Travelling, Open-fronted, Knocking

9. Oxer, Gate, Parallel, Clinker, Planks, Brush, Water, Spread, Upright

10. Trigger, Champion, Boris, Golden Flame, Flicka, Ed, Black Beauty, Seabiscuit, Phar Lap, Spirit

Spot the difference!

Can you spot the 15 differences between these two pictures?

Turn to page 98 for the answers!

PULLING POWER!

We all love riding ponies – but horses and ponies are also brilliant at pulling things – from logs to carriages!

HARROWING

This beautiful young Shire horse is learning to pull a harrow, so he can work for the farmer in the fields. Heavy horses used to be the tractors of yesteryear, when horses were the only (and brilliant!) way of working the land and getting heavy jobs done. Imagine how long it would have taken people to plough and harvest crops without horses!

LOG ON

This is Moony. Moony is a logging cob! Horses and ponies always used to haul logs which were cut down, and clear land for building – but this work was taken over by tractors. However, horses and ponies are again popular for this work where tractors would destroy the land. They provide low-impact pulling power where vegetation and land needs to be protected.

WATER HORSE

Canals were built to transport goods all over the country – and canal boats were pulled by horses. Nowadays, this gentle way of seeing the countryside can still be enjoyed as enthusiasts use strong cobs to pull their narrowboats along the waterways. The horses need to be calm and steady – just like Buddy here.

RACING PONIES

It's not all work! The sport of scurry driving is popular, where pairs of ponies race against the clock through a course of cones. It's a thrilling spectacle – see it at all the top shows!

GO GYPSY!

If you fancy a holiday with a difference, how about a horse-drawn caravan? This restored gypsy caravan is hired out to holiday makers – together with a horse to tow it! What a fantastic way to see the countryside – and a great way to bond with an equine friend over several days.

SMALL YET POWERFUL

Who says horsepower has to come in big sizes? The Shetland pony is renowned for its strength – despite its small stature. This one is pulling two adults with ease at a spanking trot!

SMART COBS

Other tradesmen also used cobs and horses to deliver their wares to customers. This butcher's turnout at a show has a good-looking coloured cob. High-stepping cobs were not only impressive to look at, but they delivered meat to customers without delay in a time before refrigeration.

Shire horses have always been popular to transport beer from the brewery to the pubs – and today many breweries keep Shires to attend shows and publicise their trade. The strength of the Shire horse, coupled with its legendary good nature, makes it the ideal public relations officer!

ALL ABOARD!

MINE'S A PINT!

The stagecoach was the long-distance coach of its day, with teams of hardworking horses changed frequently between the vast distances travelled. Look out for pubs on stage routes which would have had livery stables at the back, for housing replacement horses. This was good for trade – weary travellers made eager customers!

WHAT IS HORSEPOWER?

Do you know what is meant by the term horsepower which people use when they talk about cars and other machines? Engineer James Watt measured horsepower at 33,000 foot-pounds of work in one minute. This means one horse raising coal (from a mine for instance) can raise 330 pounds of coal 100 feet in a minute, or 33 pounds of coal 1,000 feet in one minute. One horsepower is equivalent to 746 watts.

ROAD RANGER

Riding on the roads is sometimes unavoidable. Follow our guide to signals, being seen and staying safe!

IS IT NECESSARY?

Riding on the road is not recommended, and if it can be avoided, it is best to. Sometimes it is necessary to get to the nearest common or bridlepaths, but before you ride on the road ask yourself whether there is another route that you can take to get to the best hacking area without using roads. Are there fields or commonland adjacent to the road that you could ride on instead? (Be aware that some farmers' fields are out of bounds to horses!)

ROAD SAFETY ITEMS

There are many reflective and bright road safety items available for both you and your pony. Wearing as many as possible will give you the most visibility and therefore increase your safety.
  At the very least a fluorescent tabard should be worn by you.

For you...
● Reflective or fluorescent tabard

● Reflective coat

● Reflective hat cover

● Reflective chaps

● Reflective armbands

For your pony...
● A ride-on reflective rug

● Reflective brushing boots

● Reflective cheekpiece and browband covers

THINGS TO CONSIDER

Some factors you need to consider before riding on the roads to ensure you will be safe include:

The volume of traffic. The time of day can heavily influence this. For example, try to avoid rush hours or times you know to be busy (like straight after school). Avoid busy roads, try to opt for a quieter route. The fewer cars there are, the fewer hazards for you.

The speed of traffic. Cars are more likely to be travelling faster on main roads so avoid these. Sticking to smaller roads and lanes is better, as traffic should be travelling at a slower pace.

Is there a grass verge? You can ride on grass verges, it is preferable to being on the road with cars. Just be aware if the grass on the verge is long as the ground may be uneven, and take care if the verge is narrow, as if a pony shies he may go into the road. Also, never canter on a grass verge, however tempting!

Can you be easily seen? Being clearly visible to other road users is essential and makes you a lot more safe. Check out the list of road safety items to make sure you have all the right gear before you step out on the roads!

Ready for the road

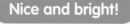

Nice and bright!

BEING CONSIDERATE

It is important to remember that cars have the right to be on the roads as well as you so ride in a quiet and sensible fashion. Remember to thank motorists who are considerate to you, but keep in mind that not all drivers will understand ponies as well as you, so could drive too close or go past you too fast. It is up to you to use hand signals and gestures to explain what you would like the driver to do.

SIGNALS

THANK YOU

Take your reins in one hand (your outside hand) and lift your free hand up to around shoulder height with your palm facing outward, as if you were about to wave. Keep your hand raised for a couple of seconds, then gather your reins again.

If it is unsafe to take your hands off the reins, just look at the driver, smile and nod your head forwards. Perhaps mime the words, "thank you" if you like!

SLOW DOWN

Take you reins in your outside hand and hold your other arm out with your palm facing down. Wave your arm up and down slowly.

PLEASE PASS WIDE AND SLOW

INDICATING

Hold out your left arm (extended from the shoulder, hand flat and palm to the front) if you are going left, and your right arm to the side if you are going right, holding your reins in the opposite hand. Make your signals strong so motorists can understand your intentions.

STOP

To ask a motorist to stop, turn from the waist (as best you can and only if safe) to face them, extend your arm out and hold your hand up so they are looking at your palm.

TO FIND OUT MORE ABOUT RIDING AND ROAD SAFETY VISIT

www.bhs.org.uk

A Timeless Bond

How a bond between horse and owner proves too strong to break

PONY short story winner!

By Elissa Dallimore

The vast stillness of the desert land is shifting ever so slightly and the rising heat clouds my view of the timeless distance. Suddenly, all is disturbed by the movement of hooves kicking up the rich desert sand, eyes alert and ears pricked. The drinkers-of-the-wind know this land better than any man, for they are the beautiful and ancient Arabian horses.

"Farah... Farah...!" My mother's anxious voice shakes me from my horsey daydream.

"Coming Mama," I reply, and my hands tremble as I remember what today is. Today, my brother Dhakir is to compete in the local horse race of a mile distance. I should feel excited, there are only four other competitors in the race, so the chances of Dhakir winning are promising. However, if my brother does not win the race, the winner could take some of our sheep, or possessions, or even require service of one of our horses. This is a price my family cannot afford to pay.

I slowly walk into my tent and see my mother has laid out an elegant long, blue dress for me to wear because of the occasion. It fits perfectly, yet I don't like myself as I look into a small mirror and I rearrange my shawl so no-one can see my long, dark hair. Once I am finished, I go to my mother who is fixing her own shawl. As I walk in she looks up and smiles.

"You look beautiful, dear," she says, and then turns back to the mirror.

"Thank you," I mumble.

"You can ride your horse to the race if you would like," suggests my mother, and my mood lightens at the thought of this.

"Oh thank you, Mama! I shall go and ready her," I respond, smiling as I give her a quick hug. Not too far away from the tent I see my horse, her flea-bitten grey coat glistening in the sunlight. As soon as she hears her name Amal lifts her head and comes trotting gracefully over to me. Her eyes are kind and her steady breath soon calms me.

I have been to many horse races before, but I have never felt as nervous as I do now. Amal shifts underneth me, her ears flicking back at me as she can sense my tension. I try to give her a reassuring pat, but as I see my father step out and raise the flag for the riders to come forth, my whole body seems to go numb. For about five seconds there is a buzzing noise in my ear as the crowd holds its breath, then my father drops the flag and the horses and riders are off!

The chances of Dhakir winning the race are promising

Soon I spot Dhakir in third place, and my spirits rise knowing he will save his horse's speed for the end. As they race on into the distance, all I see is a blur. Hours seem to pass when it is only minutes before they reappear again – yet I see only three riders return, and my brother is not one of them. My heart races as they cross the finish line, my eyes frantically scanning the area for Dhakir. I ride over towards my mother and father but before I can ask where my brother is, I see my parents race towards a figure leading a horse. Dhakir's ankle is twisted at an awkward angle, and his face is white.

"A big lizard... ran out... spooked her... couldn't stay on..." he manages to say, still gasping for breath. My mother looks over his ankle which is already swollen to twice its normal size. I dismount and take both Amal and Dhakir's horse back to our tent. How could this happen? What would happen now?

I am so busy thinking these thoughts and taking care of the horses that I did not notice my family arrive. My father's voice makes me jump as he greets the winner who has come to claim his prize. He seems uninterested in any of our possessions until he sees Amal. Then, his eyes light up like fire.

"Is this your horse, Sir?" he asks, addressing my father as he strokes Amal's neck.

"Yes. Well, more like my daughter's horse," my father replies, chuckling. However, the man does not seem to notice the joke.

"I see how poor your family is, and therefore I require very little," the man sneers. Relief floods my mind until he speaks again. "I will only require the service of your horse in a raid our camp has planned."

At first the words do not register, but slowly and painfully the truth settles in. He wants to take my beloved Amal, my only real friend. No, it isn't possible. How can this nightmare be true? I look wide-eyed to each face in my family, but their eyes show only sorrow.

"The horse can stay with you tonight as she will need to be well rested for tomorrow's journey," the man proposes, before taking his leave of us.

I stay as still as a statue until my brother speaks. "I am sorry, Farah," Dhakir murmers, his eyes downcast and heavy with sorrow.

"Sorry? You are sending Amal to her death and all you can think to say is sorry?" Anger bubbles in my stomach and I feel the heat begining to rise into my face.

"Farah, please, we should be thankful he didn't take our camel, or any of our sheep," pleads my mother, gently.

"She is not going to her death, Farah, they will take care of her during the raid," my father adds.

"You saw the way he flogged his own poor horse,

You are sending Amal to her death...

Father. We can't let him take her," I cry, as tears form in my eyes.

"There is nothing we can do, and you know that Farah, but I promise I will find you a better horse," says Dhakir.

"I only want Amal!" I spit, shaking with uncontrollable fury.

"Farah, stop acting so childishly." My mother's voice turns stern.

"Why don't you settle Amal for the night. Then she will have a much better chance in the raid tomorrow," my father suggests to me.

I lead Amal out of the tent without another word and soon the tears start streaming down my face. Then I feel a nudge at my arm and turn around to see Amal looking at me with her head tilted. I laugh as her lower lip starts to wiggle, just as it did when she was a foal. I remember as clear as water, the first day I met her.

It had been the worst drought I had experienced in my short nine years of life. My mouth felt like paper as I had very little water to spare. Not too far off I heard a short whinny of distress and immediately I set off in that direction, not caring that the hot sand was scorching my feet. It wasn't long before I came across a skinny two-year-old filly, all alone. At first she was wary of me, but thirst soon overcame her fear and she drank the last of my goat's milk. I knew I couldn't give up on her and my father allowed me to keep her on condition that I would care for her.

Eventually, we earned each other's trust, and even became good friends. From then on we were inseparable. I gave her the Arabic name Amal, for she had never lost hope and, against all odds had survived in the desert before I had found her. As I began to feed her dates, I knew that I would do whatever it took to keep us together.

Despite the hot days in the desert, nights are always very cold. The sun has not yet begun to rise as I creep towards my saddle bag, shivering. These shivers, however, come more from the preparation for our escape than from the cold. Slowly I creep back towards the tent that Amal and I share. Amal seems to have noticed my absence and is already up on her hooves.

After a quick brush, I saddle and bridle her. A wave of guilt washes over me as I mount. It is almost a crime for an Arabian horse to be laden with a burden, even with one as small as mine. I cannot bear to look back towards my family's tent, knowing the pain I will put them through once they awake.

First, we head towards higher ground so we can look over the desert in search of an oasis. I open my eyes to search and look around us. Not too far off I spot vegetation, which is a clear sign that an oasis will not be far off. Soon we reach the vegetation and follow it until it leads us to water. Here I give Amal a groom and we both enjoy a long drink from the pure water.

"Oh Amal, whatever will we do now?" I sigh. Amal looks at me and sneezes as the wind starts to pick up. I rub her neck as I look at the sky and to my surprise I see that the sky is turning almost a sandy colour. When the wind becomes suddenly very strong I put two-and-two together: a sandstorm is coming. My heart begins to race and I know Amal's only chance of survival is to flee with the other horses, without me. I race away from the oasis with Amal following, and then I stop and see Amal already prancing.

"Amal go! Follow the other horses and get as far away from here as possible!" I insist, before giving her one final hug. She stops and won't go any further. Then a herd of horses, heading away from danger, pass by. Dhakir's horse whinnies to her and Amal's instincts take over. To my relief she heads towards them, and together they gallop away.

I stand there watching them until a wind blows so strong that it almost knocks me over, and I race back towards the oasis. Quickly I grab my saddlebag and run towards higher ground and by the time I reach it I can see the sandy-coloured cloud forming in the distance. I adjust my shawl so it covers my face, then I curl up in a ball, covering the back of my head with my saddlebag. As the sandstorm races towards me I worry about Amal. Did she have enough time to get away? I begin to understand that there is something more important than us staying together – our safety!

The sandstorm lasts for a few hours and when it is finally over, I feel as though I can barely move. I am completely covered from head-to-toe in sand, but that does not seem to matter. All I care about is finding Amal. I find my way back to the oasis and fall asleep as soon as I sit down. The next day I awake to the sound of hooves kicking up the desert sand and immediately, I spring awake. The herd races back to camp and I am relieved to see that it seems like all of the horses made it. My eyes search for Amal but I cannot see her and my heart feels as though it has stopped as I sit down with my face heavy in my hands.

Suddenly, I feel a nudge at my arm and, whipping around, I see Amal behind me, her head tilted, her lower lip wiggling.

"If we can get through this then we can get through anything," I whisper to Amal, and we slowly make our way back towards our real home.

> Amal's only chance of survival is to flee with the other horses, without me

Head

Chin up, the rider is looking where she is going, towards the next jump. Looking ahead keeps the rider in a positive frame of mind, and influences the pony, too. Looking down encourages a refusal so look up and throw your heart over that jump!

Body

The rider folds forward at the waist, allowing the shoulders to drop down to the pony's shoulders. The rider is NOT standing up in her stirrups. Instead, she is folding towards her pony in a safe, balanced and secure position.

Hands

Folding forward enables the hands to follow the pony's head. This means the pony has the freedom of his head and neck to get a good jump, and he will have confidence that his rider won't jab him in the mouth. The rider's elbows have some bend, ensuring the rider has soft hands, and she can move them back towards her again as she lands so she does not lose her contact and control.

Get the

perfect jump!

What's the perfect jumping position? Follow our guide to looking (and feeling) great over jumps – whether show jumping or riding across country!

Legs

Knees are bent, soft and supple. Lower leg is close to the girth, weight in the heel. This ensures a secure seat and is essential for good jumping. The rider is in the perfect position to use her legs, and if her pony does slow down or threaten to stop, she can not only push him on, but she won't go sailing over his head if he ignores her!

Not forgetting the pony!

Because his rider has a great jumping position, the pony is able to jump well, arching his back to ensure he clears the jump, and is looking forward, towards his next jump.

Perfect!

Pre-jump checklist!

Before you go jumping make sure you are wearing:
● A correctly-fitted, and approved riding hat (natch!)
● A body protector
● Proper riding boots
● Gloves for good grip

Things to remember:
● You might also like to carry a whip, just in case your pony needs a reminder.
● Shorten your stirrups by two-three holes to allow you to get into your forward and jumping position.
● Fit your pony with a neck strap for some extra security if you think you might need it, or are scared you might jab him in the mouth.

Scottish ponies!

The ponies of Scotland rock! They're hardy, look cute and are easily recognisable!

The Scottish Highland pony

The biggest of the Scottish ponies, the Highland boasts Viking ponies in its ancestry, and is a gorgeous, cuddly native that's perfect for children and adults to ride!

- Max height 14.2hh. They are heavily built, with an abundance of coat to withstand the harsh Scottish climate.
- Coat colours: Grey, bay, black. Some are dark chestnut (bloodstone) with a striking silver mane and tail, and many ponies have a dorsal stripe and some show zebra markings on the legs and shoulders.
- Line of work: Sure-footed, strong and calm, the Highland pony is brilliant to ride over the Scottish Highlands. It is still the best way for hunters to get deer home from the moors.
- The Highland pony is considered *At Risk* (between only 900-1500 left) by the Rare Breeds Survival Trust.

DYK?

Her Majesty The Queen breeds Highlands at her Balmoral Stud, and her ponies often take the ribbons at shows up and down the country. The royal Highlands earn their living – some carry shot stags in the traditional manner, others carry panniers when grouse shooting takes place. They also take visitors for treks around the royal estate. Her Majesty is the Patron of the Highland Pony Society.

The Shetland pony

Everyone is familiar with the smallest of our native breeds, the Shetland pony. Small in stature but big in personality, the Shetland is unmistakable, and is famous for thrilling audiences in The Shetland Pony Grand National, the final of which takes place at Olympia at Christmas!

DYK?

In the past, Shetland ponies have been highly valued as a pit pony, spending their lives working hard in the coal mines. Today they are popular as riding and driving ponies, and are real characters!

- Max height: 42 Inches. Shetlands under 35 inches are considered miniatures. Shetland ponies are measured in inches, not hands.
- Coat colour: Black, grey, bay, skewbald and piebald. Shetlands are the only native pony permitted to be broken-coloured.
- The Shetland has a waterproof double coat, to withstand the harsh Shetland climate.
- Characteristics: Courageous, intelligent and strong. Don't be fooled by its short legs; the Shetland is one of the strongest ponies in proportion to its size!

DYK?

The Eriskay pony

- Height: Between 12hh to 13.2hh.
- Coat colours: Usually grey, occasionally black and bay
- Like all Scottish ponies, Eriskays grow a very dense waterproof coat to survive the winter – although they grow hardly any feather on their heels.
- Characteristics: This pony loves human company!

The Eriskay is an original native pony from the Western Isles of Scotland, and takes its name from the island of the same name. They were used to pull carts, plough fields, carry heavy loads and even take children to school, and although they are not very tall they are strong enough to be ridden by a small adult.

The Eriskay pony is classed as *Critical* by the Rare Breeds Trust, but enthusiasts are working to increase numbers and awareness.

On a roll!

Horses and ponies just love a good roll!

Fly protection

Horses and ponies may paw the ground to dig up the dust, and then roll in it. Why? It could be a good way to clear their coat from insects and itches, and offer them some protection against annoying flies.

Sweaty!

A horse or pony will often roll when turned out after being ridden – it's a great way to rub out the feel of the saddle and get rid of the sweat!

Drying off

If you want your pony to stay clean, don't turn him out in the field or put him in the stable when he's still wet after a bath. The chances are he'll drop to his knees and roll himself dry (and dirty!).

Goody!

Horses and ponies roll because it feels good!

Pooh!

One reason why ponies roll after a bath is to try and get the smell of the shampoo out of their coats. What better way to smell like one of the herd than to cover yourself in dirt and dust?

Water horses

Some horses and ponies are real water babies, and will try to roll in muddy puddles and streams – even when their riders are still in the saddle!

If your pony starts pawing the ground don't think he's cute – ride him on strongly to avoid him rolling. Not only could he roll on *you*, but he could break the tree on your saddle, so it's not quite the joke it may at first seem!

What an effort!

Can your pony roll right over onto his other side? It can take quite a bit of effort, and not all ponies make it, so they have to get up and drop to the other side, to make sure both sides are properly done!

Feet first!

Did you know that all equines get up after a roll front feet first. Cows, however, get up hind legs first!

Getting stuck

Beware – rolling in a small stable can be dangerous for ponies if they roll over and get stuck close to a wall. This is known as getting cast, and if it happens, never go into the stable and try to right your pony yourself. You could get seriously hurt if your pony panics. Always get help.

When rolling is bad

Not all rolling is fun. If your pony is sweating, looking around at his belly and rolling a lot then call the vet immediately as the chances are he is suffering from colic and is rolling in pain.

London ho

The Four Bronze Horses of Helios
Created by Rudy Weller in 1992, these four horses – Pyrois, Eos, Aethon and Phlegon – pulled Greek God of the Sun Helios through the sky. See it on the corner of Piccadilly Circus and The Haymarket. It's awesome!

Horse's head, Marble Arch
Created by Nic Fiddian-Green, this modern sculpture is huge! When made dirty by pigeons, recently, the artist himself cleaned it up!

Riders in Hyde Park
There are several riding schools in London – two based right next to Hyde Park. See riders hacking around Rotten Row, a traditional ride since the park was created.

The King's Troop, Royal Horse Artillery
The King's Troop recently moved from its home at St John's Wood to shiny new barracks in Greenwich. Truly city-based and handy for all their duties.

Police horses
Often spotted at football matches, but also seen riding around the capital, keeping a beady eye on things.

Richard the Lionheart
Sited outside Westminster is this impressive statue of Richard I, brandishing his sword.

Photos: David Burrows, Pres Panayotov, Vladimir Korostyshevskly, Klev.victor, Anton Balazh, aGinger, Dutourdinonde Photography/Shutterstock.com

‑ses

No horses in the city of London, right? Wrong! London is *teeming* with horses (some real, some not so real!) – you just need to know where to look. Here are some of them...

Statue of Boadicea
Sculpted by Thomas Thornycroft in 1902, this homage to the Iceni warrior queen overlooks the Thames and traffic at Westminster Pier.

Household Cavalry
Stationed at Knightsbridge, opposite Hyde Park, you may see the Cavalry exercising their horses early in the morning, or in the Park. You can also visit the Household Cavalry Museum at Whitehall.

Other horses to see in London

- *Whistlejacket*. The life-size portrait of this wonderful horse by Stubbs hangs in the National Gallery. Go see!
- Animals in War Memorial, Hyde Park. A tribute to all the animals who served and gave their lives in war.
- City farms. Mudchute, Vauxhall and Surrey Docks all have horses and ponies. Google for more info and opening details.

The Royal Mews
These Cleveland Bays belonging to Her Majesty are transporting members of the Royal Family to the State Opening of Parliament. The Mews is behind Buckingham Palace and is open to the public!

Spotting horses in London

Why not see how many horse statues you can see when you next visit the capital? How many are life-size? How many carry famous people? How many have small details missing – and why? For example, the wonderful rearing horses on Boadicea's statue in Westminster have no reins. How would she control them? The statue of The Duke of Wellington and his horse outside the Royal Exchange, has no saddle or stirrups – indeed the Duke isn't even wearing boots! This is because triumphal Roman Generals would have ridden this way.

What other wonderful horse paintings can you find? How about horses depicted at the National Army Museum, or in other museums and galleries? Once you start spotting, you'll get carried away!

Quiz!

TRAVEL TRAUMA!

How much do you know about travelling your pony? Try our quiz and find out!

Prep...

1. How should you prepare your trailer before asking your pony to go in it?

A: Ensure all the connections are working, that it is balanced, and that it is securely hitched to the back of the car.

B: Muck it out and give it a bit of a spruce up.

C: Check the flooring is sound, and that it is in good order, safe for your pony to travel in.

2. How should you prepare your pony for travelling?

A: Make sure he has eaten his breakfast and is wearing a strong headcollar.

B: Dress him in his best rug, with your initials on it, and plait his tail.

C: Dress him in a lightweight rug, leg wraps and tail guard, to protect him in transit.

Right or wrong?

3. What is wrong with this tail bandage?

. . . .

4. How many things can you see wrong with this picture?

. . . .

. . . .

. . . .

. . . .

. . . .

. . . .

. . . .

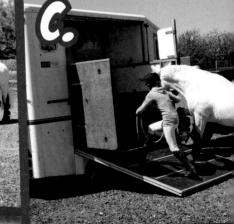

5. Which of these is the correct way to approach a ramp with your pony?

. . . .

Why, why, why?

6. This pony is in his trailer, but the ramp is still down, even though the doors are shut. Why do you think this might be?

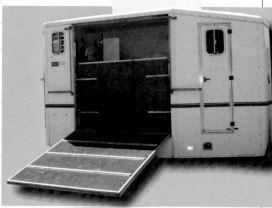

A: Because the trailer is at a show, and it is a safe way to give your pony some air.

B: Because the ramp should be put up at the last minute.

C: Because ponies like to look out of a trailer.

7. Should ponies have a haynet when travelling?

A: No. Eating while travelling could upset their stomach and give them colic.

B: Yes. It gives them something to think about, and ponies should eat little and often.

C: No – the seeds can get in their coats, which means they won't look their best when they get to a show.

8. Which of these is the principal reason why ponies may become bad travellers and be reluctant to load?

A: Forgetting to leave the trailer light on when travelling.

B: The driver forgetting to slow down and drive extra smoothly.

C: Ponies don't like shows very much.

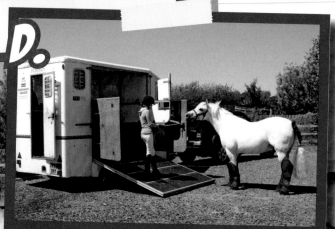

HOW DID YOU DO? TURN TO PAGE 98 FOR THE ANSWERS!

Charlie does a Bungee jump!

THAT LOOKS SO COOL. I'LL BE FIGHTING OFF THE FILLIES IF I DO A BUNGEE JUMP!

YES, HI! I WANT TO BOOK A BUNGEE JUMP. TOMORROW? GREAT!

SO, HAVE YOU BUNGEE'D BEFORE?

ER... YEAH. TWICE ACTUALLY!

100 m

COOL! SO YOU'LL WANT TO DO THE 200 METRES, RIGHT?

100 m

200 m

ER... YEAH. SURE!

WHAT AM I DOING? WHAT AM I THINKING? I HATE HEIGHTS!

SO, ARE YOU READY MY MAN?

I DON'T THINK I CAN DO IT, I'M SCARED OF HEIGHTS!

BUT YOUR GIRL IS DOWN THERE WATCHING YOU.

YOU'RE RIGHT. OKAY, I'LL GO ON THREE. ONE, TWO...

THREE!

AAARRGGGGHHHHHHH!!!!!!

ACTUALLY, THIS ISN'T SO BAD.

HERE I GO AGAIN!!!!!!

YEAH! RIDE IT MAN!

CAN SOMEONE GET ME DOWN PLEASE?

CHARLIE, THAT LOOKED LIKE SO MUCH FUN!

FUN... OH YEAH! I CAN'T WAIT TO GO AGAIN!

The rider by the folly

Did Zara really see what she *thought* she saw?

Strange stories have always surrounded the folly at the top of the hill. The livery yard where I keep my pony Morris stood on the site of an old estate. The big house had long since gone and no trace remained but the folly, a tower built like a fairy turret, still stood proud, casting a long shadow across the grass on sunny days, looking like a film set on moonlit nights.

> "He built the folly for his wife," my friend Anna told me.

"The owner of the big house built the folly for his wife," my friend Anna told me. "Only one terrible day he leant over the parapet at the top, some bricks gave way and he fell, breaking his neck and her heart."

I shuddered. "Really?" I asked. "How do you know?"

"It's common knowledge," Anna said firmly.

"What happened to the wife?" I asked.

"Went mad. Spent the rest of her life riding around the folly, broken-hearted and mumbling to herself."

I looked again at the folly. Tall, forbidding, crumbling at the top. I imagined the husband falling to his death, the wife wailing, going mad. It was too creepy for words.

LATE TO THE YARD

Several months later, when the leaves were falling from the trees and a chill hung in the air, I got detention at school for wearing nail varnish. Instead of rushing to the stables after school I had to sit in a classroom with the disruptive pupils and write an essay on *Why school has rules*. Eventually I was let out, and I made it to the yard an hour late. It had been a sunny day and there was still half-an-hour of daylight left, so I hurridly saddled Morris, promising him I'd groom him when we got back, and set off alone – no-one had waited for me. I badly misjudged when the sun would set and found it was getting dark much earlier than I had hoped. I had to find a short-cut home – and the quickest route would take us past the old folly.

"Come on Morris," I said, stroking his mane, "we're not afraid of a few bricks, are we?" But the closer we got to the folly, the less brave I felt. It loomed up ahead of us, its turret pointing to the sky, made even more spooky by the moon glowing behind it. All we needed was to hear an owl hooting, I thought, grimly, and the horror movie scene would be complete.

A SUDDEN HALT

I urged Morris into trot as the path wound its way past the folly, but when we got to the other side Morris slowed abruptly to a halt, and I lurched forward, spitting out mane.

"What *are* you doing?" I asked him, pushing myself back into the saddle and regaining my dignity. But then I saw – or I thought I saw – something moving in front of us, almost floating silently on the swirling evening mist, not touching the ground, the folly as a backdrop.

> But the closer we got to the folly, the less brave I felt

A PALE HORSE

It was a woman on a pale horse. She was riding side saddle and wore a blue velvet habit, a feather on her top hat bobbing as she followed the movement of her horse.

As I looked and blinked the haunting sound of sobbing reached my ears, sending a shiver down my spine.

THE LONG WAY HOME...

Abruptly, I turned Morris, urging him into a gallop along the path, retracing our steps. I hung on, deciding the long way home would be a good idea after all.

By the time we reached the yard darkness had fallen and once in the warm glow of the stable lights I wondered whether my eyes had played a trick on me in the moonlight. Had I really seen what I thought had been there? Or had I just been imagining things? Morris hadn't seemed too bothered – maybe he hadn't seen anything, perhaps there had been nothing there to see. But why had he stopped in the first place?

To this day I can't decide whether the ghostly figure of the weeping woman had really appeared at the folly, or whether I'd imagined her. Which is why I never told anyone about my experience. It's my secret, and I'll never betray the woman on her pale horse – the woman I thought I saw.

A woman on a pale horse...

posed by models

TO LOAN OR

HI GUYS!

HI ELLA, ARE YOU COMING ON A HACK WITH US TODAY?

HI!

NO, SORRY. MY MUM HAS FORBIDDEN ME TO HACK, SHE THINKS IT'S TOO DANGEROUS. SHE THINKS EVERYTHING TO DO WITH PONIES IS TOO DANGEROUS, ACTUALLY.

OH NO!

HI ELLA, WHY ARE YOU NOT OUT ON A HACK WITH RYAN AND JACK?

MY MUM DOESN'T WANT ME TO GO ON HACKS. SHE THINKS IT'S DANGEROUS. SHE DOESN'T LIKE ME RIDING AT ALL REALLY.

THAT'S A SHAME. ESPECIALLY AS NIMBLE IS UP FOR LOAN, I THINK HE'D BE PERFECT FOR YOU!

I'D LOVE THAT! BUT I DOUBT MY MUM WOULD EVER LET ME.

I WONDER WHERE THE OTHERS WENT ON THEIR HACK? I BET THEY'VE BEEN FOR A GOOD GALLOP!

WE'RE BACK!

WE HAD AN AMAZING RIDE!

NOT TO LOAN?

...AVOURITE PONY AT HER RIDING SCHOOL. BUT ELLA'S MUM THINKS...
...ER FRIENDS CONVINCE HER MUM THAT PONIES ARE AWESOME?

SEE YOU LATER!

OH NIMBLE, I WISH I COULD TAKE YOU OUT ON HACKS.

ANYWAY, NIMBLE'S TACK NEEDS A CLEAN BEFORE YOUR LESSON LATER.

OKAY.

I SO WISH I COULD LOAN NIMBLE. I WOULD KEEP HIS TACK SQUEAKY CLEAN!

WHAT'S WRONG, ELLA?

KAREN SAYS NIMBLE IS UP FOR LOAN! I REALLY WANT TO LOAN HIM BUT MY MUM WOULD NEVER LET ME!

YOU HAVE TO LOAN NIMBLE! IMAGINE HOW MUCH FUN WE WOULD ALL HAVE RIDING TOGETHER ALL THE TIME!

WE'LL FIND A WAY TO CONVINCE YOUR MUM!

SHE RARELY EVEN GETS OUT OF THE CAR WHEN SHE COMES TO COLLECT ME, SHE DOESN'T LIKE PONIES AND HATES ME RIDING!

OMG!

RIGHT! LET'S THINK... WHAT CAN WE DO TO CONVINCE ELLA'S MUM SHE SHOULD LOAN NIMBLE?

GET HER TO COME AND WATCH HER LESSON, THEN SHE'LL SEE HOW GOOD SHE AND NIMBLE ARE TOGETHER.

SHE WON'T COME ONTO THE YARD, SHE WAITS IN THE CAR WHEN SHE COLLECTS ME.

ANYWAY, I'VE GOT TO GRO[O]... NIMBLE READY FOR MY LES[SON]...

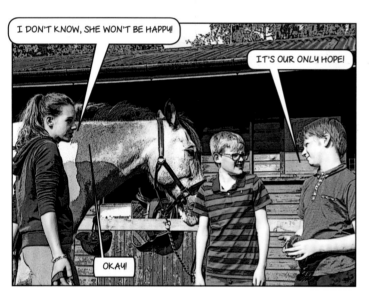

I DON'T KNOW, SHE WON'T BE HAPPY!

IT'S OUR ONLY HOPE!

OKAY!

HI MUM, CAN YOU PICK ME UP AT THREE O'CLOCK PLEASE? I'LL BE READY THEN.

HI, HAVE YOU BOYS SEEN ELLA?

OH HI, JULIA! YES, SHE'S IN THE SCHOOL, RIDING A LOVELY PONY CALLED NIMBLE!

WELL, SHE'S RUNNING VERY LATE! SHE SAID SHE'D BE READY!

ELLA, YOU'RE LATE!

ACTUALLY MUM, I ASKED YOU TO COME EARLY SO YOU COUL[D] WATCH ME RIDE NIMBLE. HE'S FOR LOAN YOU SEE. I KNEW [YOU] WOULD NEVER LET ME LOAN HIM, SO WE THOUGHT YOU COU[LD] MEET NIMBLE AND LOVE HIM LIKE I DO!

ELLA

KAREN

JACK

RYAN

JULIA

STARRING: HATTIE AS ELLA, DYLAN AS RYAN, LUCAS AS JACK, DEBBIE AS KAREN AND NADINE AS JULIA. PLUS BUBBLES, ALFIE AND MINNIE THE PONIES! LOCATION: SPRINGWOOD STABLES, HANTS.

WE'LL WORK ON A PLAN!

I'VE GOT IT! ELLA, TELL YOUR MUM TO COLLECT YOU A BIT EARLY, SO WHEN SHE ARRIVES YOU'LL BE IN YOUR LESSON ON NIMBLE.

YES! THEN SHE'LL HAVE TO COME INTO THE YARD TO FIND YOU, SEE YOU RIDING NIMBLE AND FALL IN LOVE WITH HIM!

QUICK, GET TO THE SCHOOL, YOU NEED TO WARM NIMBLE UP SO HE'S GOING WELL WHEN YOUR MUM ARRIVES!

LOVELY, ELLA! NIMBLE IS GOING VERY NICELY.

WELL I'M VERY UPSET YOU LIED TO ME, BUT I CAN SEE THAT THIS PONY MEANS A LOT TO YOU, AND YOU LOOK LIKE YOU'VE PUT A LOT OF HARD WORK INTO YOUR RIDING.

I HAVE, BUT IT'S ALL DOWN TO NIMBLE, HE'S AN AMAZING PONY!

HE DOES SEEM RATHER FRIENDLY! MAYBE I'LL HAVE A CHAT TO KAREN.

GUESS WHAT? I CAN LOAN NIMBLE! OUR PLAN WORKED!

THAT'S SO GREAT!

WAHOOO!

THE END!!!

57

Make a model pony feed room!

Our model pony feed room has everything you need to keep your model ponies well fed and happy!

You will need
- A cardboard box. Ours held paper!
- Extra cardboard and a small box
- Paint
- Yoghurt pots (extra small and individual size)
- A dishcloth
- Net bags from oranges and garlic
- Wool or string
- Modelling clay
- Yellow sponge
- Hay
- Pulses
- Scissors, paint brushes, sticky tape and glue.

How to do it!

1 Cut your box so that you have an open side where you can play with your model feed room. Cut a window out of your box and then paint the inside in the colour of your choice.

2. Paint the outside walls of your feed room in whatever colour you like. Ours are soft grey.

4 Cut an opening into the smaller box and paint this. Then place your sink in the opening and glue in place. One sink unit – sorted!

3 Your feed room will need a sink! Take a tiny yoghurt pot and cut it in half, pushing the bottom inside the top to make a smaller container. Now take some corrugated plastic from a sandwich container to make the draining board and stick together. Paint your sink silver.

Make feed bins from yoghurt pots (square ones are best), and cut out some lids from cardboard. Paint these, add the lids with a piece of sticky tape then fill with rice or a soup pulse mix (course mix!).

Make some feed sacks out of dishcloths or old jute. Fill with some rice or soup pulses and sew up.

Haynets can be made from the orange and garlic nets. Snip them to the right size and thread wool or string through the holes to make a net. Fill with hay. The small holes in the garlic nets make good haynets for haylage or for model ponies who need their hay intake monitored!

Yellow sponges cut and tied with string make great haybales.

Finally, from modelling clay make a chopping board, some apples and carrots to add to your feed room. You can even make a feed scoop and some rats!

Print out some floor and roof tiles from the computer, stick them to your floor and to a piece of cardboard for your roof, and your feed room is ready to be used! Print out a feed chart, too!

Colour match!

Do you and your fave pony have a colour scheme? Here are some amazing examples to inspire you!

Tangerine dream

Now, the question is, did this rider gain her tangerine inspiration from her own coat, or her pony's bandages? Or maybe the trigger was her orange-and-white pony!

Pretty in pink

Georgina has cleverly matched her own pink t-shirt with Lily's pink numnah and gorgeous pink-and-white browband. Cute!

Lovely lavender

Another clever use of equine legwear – Benji's tendon boots have flashes of lavender, to tie-in with his rider's lavender outfit. Subtle, but classy!

Deep purple

More lavender – this time the pony's rug, headcollar and rope blend with the darker purple tubs. Don't forget your pony's stable fixtures and fittings when planning your colour scheme. Oh, and his grooming brushes!

Singing in blues

This pair are ready to travel in style with their matching pale blue outfits. No mistaking which pony and human make up this particular partnership!

Feeling rosy

Hacking out, or going on a sponsored ride is the perfect excuse to dress up in your colours. How about rose pink, as seen here?

Be seen

Don't forget your reflective gear! There are some fabulous clothes with reflective detail on – such as the stars on this rider's hat silk, arms and chaps. The reflective body protector is a brilliant way to ensure drivers can see you on the road – it's just as important to wear reflective clothing on a sunny day as in fading light. Dark shadows under trees can make it difficult for drivers to see ponies and horses until the very last minute!

Go west

Exactly how cool is this Western barrel-racer's outfit and tack? They're a proper match made in heaven!

Hmmm-could do better

This is a case of clashing colours. Can you imagine how brilliant this rider's top would look if she were riding an Appaloosa? More thought needed!

Make an effort

Does your favourite riding school pony have a coloured saddle cloth? Why not co-ordinate next time you ride him, by wearing a matching sweat shirt?

Other ways with colour

Look out for amazing accessories – coloured hoof glitter, sparkly mane and tail extensions, even coloured gel to paint your pony! Remember though – less is more!

Where in the world?

Can you point the pony or horse to their place of origin?

Orlov Trotter

Akhal-Teke

Fjord

Connemara

Haflinger

Waler

Morgan

Ardennais

Arab

Andalusian

Appaloosa

Boer

Freisian

Falabella

Turn to page 98 for the answers!

Perfect po

The Riders. Which of these sounds most like you?

Rider 1
- You have been riding for several years and love it!
- You can ride most of the riding school ponies
- Your favourite things to do are jumping and hacking

Rider 2
- You have just progressed to riding off the lead rein
- You are always nervous before a lesson
- Your favourite things to do are cuddling the ponies after the lesson, and practising your rising trot

The ponies

Monty is a cheeky pony with a sense of humour. He can be a bit sharp – he's nervous about anything he's not sure of, and often takes off across the school if he's scared. The best thing about Monty is that he loves jumping, and he never refuses!

Pirate is a youngster who has just been backed and broken in. He is a sweet pony but doesn't know much, and always looks to his rider to give him direction and confidence in lessons and on hacks.

The Verdict!

If you're Rider 1...

If you think you match Rider 1 then you can ride almost any pony! Although you may consider that you've moved on from riding the slower ponies, remember that a good rider can get a tune out of *any* pony, and no horses or ponies are beneath them.

Pirate would be a challenge for you – instead of the pony teaching you, it would be your job to teach Pirate, and you will learn loads! If you ride Tilly, your job would be to ensure she goes consistently, rather than in fits and starts, as she does with less experienced riders.

With Monty, your job is to give him confidence – something a nervous rider is incapable of. As for Cassidy, you should be able to demonstrate that she is capable of much more than anyone imagined!

If you're Rider 2...

You haven't had much experience, so Pirate is not the pony for you. Monty can also be nervous, so if his rider is, too, you'll scare each other!

Cassidy would be perfect for you as she will only go at the speed you ask. Once you've progressed then you could try Tilly on lessons – and with more confidence you can ride Tilly on hacks where, instead of practising your *go* aids, you can practise your *stop* ones!

Do you know which type of pony you could ride to improve your riding? Read our rider profiles, find the one which is most like you – and then decide which ponies would really help your riding!

Rider 3

- You have just progressed to a higher lesson at your riding school, learning to canter and jump
- You are a bit nervous about going up a lesson – but excited as well!
- You're really looking forward to your very first jumping lesson!

Rider 4

- You have been on the same lesson at your riding school for ages
- You actually get a bit bored on lessons
- Your favourite things to do are... well, actually, you don't really have any

Posed by models

Cassidy is a versatile pony who can be ridden by beginners or more experienced riders. Her behaviour mirrors that of her riders – if they can't be bothered, then neither can Cassidy – but if they can, she wakes up and gets stuck in!

Tilly has been at the riding school for years, and is a steady, confidence-giver. She is very lazy, and her riders have to work hard to get her going on lessons! Tilly can often surprise her riders on hacks – one minute she's eating the grass, the next minute she's cantering to keep up!

If you're Rider 3...

You're up for a challenge – and turn any nerves you might have into excitement! You may think you've progressed beyond Cassidy, but trying her again may surprise you. Can you get her going better than you did when you were a beginner?

Monty would be a challenge for you, too. If you can handle his mood swings, he'll take you jumping! Although it wouldn't be fair on Pirate to ride him just yet, you could aim to progress to a young pony, and see if you can teach *him*, instead of the other way around!

If you're Rider 4...

You really need to push yourself and make the most out of every single moment of your lessons. Trying different ponies may shake you up a bit, and make you realise how you can progress – if you try!

Don't nod off on Tilly but see whether you can wake her up – and why not give Cassidy another chance? If you find her slow, it's because you're not working hard enough. She's brilliant for you because the more effort you put in, the more Cassidy responds!

TITAN

Could a horse and a boy find happiness together?

Stanley the horse never got a rest. He'd work all day and finally, at midnight, he was thrown into a very small stable with nothing but his regular meal of an apple core left over from the market and, if he was lucky, a carrot. Stanley worked on Moore Street. He'd walk to the pier and collect fruit and vegetables and bring them back in his small cart to his master, Sir Jarvis. Sir Jarvis was a very rich man. He was rich because he sold fruit and vegetables to lots of people at the market. Although he was rich, he never cared much about his working horse, Stanley. 'Why would I bother to feed a stupid animal when I can feed myself and all my family?' he thought. As you can see, Sir Jarvis was a very greedy and selfish man indeed.

A mile away from Stanley's stable was a small cottage which held eight children: Sarah, Henry, Scott, Peter, Jane, Adele, Michael and Elissa. Peter was always outside playing with wildlife, often on his own.

One day, Peter was in his back garden, trying to build a fort. He was using old planks of wood and fallen-down branches, and he noticed a swallow swoop down and steal a twig. This was the first swallow Peter had seen since spring began. He ran after it though the woods, across a field and finally ended up at a great big mansion with stone griffins on the pillars. This must have been the place Mr and Mrs McNulty, Peter's parents, had warned him about. They said Sir Jarvis did not like little children scampering around his grounds, and that he could often be a bit moody. This was the same Sir Jarvis who owned a stall on Moore Street, and was very, very wealthy.

The swallow flew into one of the eaves on a farm building. Peter couldn't help himself but to go into the building. Stanley got one day off a month and today, in April 1931, was his day off. He sensed Peter's gentle presence and whinnied softly. Peter saw the most gorgeous thing he had ever laid eyes on – a beautiful skewbald Clydesdale horse. He walked over slowly and rubbed the horse's muzzle – gently, so as not to startle him – and Stanley whinnied very softly. The sound of footsteps broke the easy silence between them. Stanley nosed Peter as if to say, *Go, you'll be caught! Quick, run!* and Peter ran out of the stable towards home.

All night Peter thought about the amazing discovery he had made that day. Would he ever see the horse again? Stanley thought the same, but no-one knew. Peter hatched a plan. He would sneak into the stable at midnight tomorrow, and no-one would see him.

So, at a quarter to midnight Peter hopped out of bed, dodging his brothers and sisters, and crept to the door. He twisted the handle carefully and went outside. It was cold, but Peter knew that when he touched the horse he would immediately feel heat. He jogged throught the woods, over the fields until he got to Cherrywood Manor. It was exactly midnight when Peter approached the stables. He ran inside but, to his surprise, the beautiful horse was nowhere to be seen. Where could he be, thought Peter.

Suddenly, the sound of heavy hooves interrupted Peter's thoughts.

"Put this scruffy pig into the stable, right William?"

"Right," agreed the stable hand.

A tall man, with big eyebrows, walked in, violently tugging the lead rein which held a frisky and frightened horse. The horse Peter had seen the day before. Suddenly, the horse stopped dead and looked curiously to

> Peter walked over slowly and rubbed the horse's muzzle – gently, so as not to startle him

where Peter was hiding. He gave a gentle neigh as though saying, *Could it really be you? I didn't think I would ever see you again.*

"Me neither," whispered Peter, caught up in his own thoughts.

"Who goes there?" William asked sternly, walking briskly over to the barrel where Peter was hiding. He was in trouble now! Peter held his breath. He could hear his heart racing in his chest.

"Who are you, and why are you here?" shouted William, loudly.

"I... I..." Peter found he could not make up a good excuse fast enough.

"Is everything all right out there?" called Sir Jarvis. A moment later, Sir Jarvis came in. "And who are you exactly?" he asked Peter.

"I'm... I'm... "

"Spit it out child, I don't have all night!"

"I'm Peter McNulty..."

"I shall tell your parents about this," said Sir Jarvis.

And he did. Peter got a right telling-off from them the next day.

"Peter, I'm really quite shocked at you," said his mother. I would never have thought in a million years that it would be you, Peter, to invade someone's privacy like that. I really am very shocked indeed!"

"But I saw the way they were treating the horse. It's awful. Please call the police or something." Peter couldn't say another word because he started sobbing. His parents knew he had a feeling for this mystery horse, but they had to do what was right.

"As your punishment," said his father, "you'll have to do your brothers' chores for two weeks. We'll make up our minds about telling anyone, but until then you can't say a word to anyone, and your mother and I will do the same."

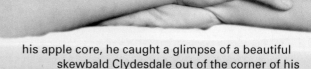

"Until then you can't say a word to anyone..."

"This isn't fair, I love him," Peter mumbled, while scraping burnt porridge off the saucepan. Peter would be 12 in a couple of weeks, but he didn't think he would be getting much for his birthday.

He caught a glimpse of a beautiful skewbald Clydesdale

Peter's birthday arrived, and Peter sat at the kitchen table eating an apple, not bothering to look out of the window at the wildlife as usual, for he was too glum. He was annoyed with himself. He couldn't help wishing he could meet the beautiful Clydesdale horse again. As Peter went to the bin beside the window with his apple core, he caught a glimpse of a beautiful skewbald Clydesdale out of the corner of his eye. Running as fast as he could out of the house, he hugged the gorgeous creature, feeding him the apple core from the palm of his hand.

"It's you, isn't it?" Peter whispered to Stanley. "I'll call you Titan!" Titan whinnied and gave Peter a nuzzle.

"So you found him," said a voice behind them. Turning around, Peter saw his mum and dad and his seven brothers and sisters.

"He's yours for ever," said his dad.

"I'll take great care of him," Peter promised, "but how did you get him?"

"Well, we called the police like you said to, and we led them to Cherrywood Manor," explained his father, "and the police took the horse and stable hand William away."

"They were looking for a willing family to take care of the horse," added his mother.

Peter ran over and gave them all a hug. "I can't thank you enough!" he told them.

"Now take great care of him," said his father.

"Oh I shall, you just wait and see!" promised Peter, with tears of happiness welling in his eyes.

Peter had many fun days after that. He even got a stall at market and sold carvings – he went around selling them from Titan's cart. Titan had a much happier life for he only had to work twice a week. With the money Peter made from the carvings he brought lots of delicious food for his family, and for Titan. As for Sir Jarvis, he was put into jail for cruelty to animals.

Now, four years on, Peter and Titan have a great business and are able to afford a fine stable and new harness. Peter grooms Titan in the morning, and exercises him in the afternoon, and the Clydesdale grazes in the field they bought behind the house. The swallow that helped Peter find Titan got a new home too – in Titan's stable – and flies along side Peter when he goes on rides. Titan has a great new life in his happy home.

Aquarius

(January 21 – February 19)
Try new things in 2015. It is not always wise to chose the devil you know, as the devil you don't know might not actually be a devil at all! If there's a school pony you've been wanting to ride, go for it! There may be a new instructor at your riding school or at Pony Club that you're apprehensive about, don't be! 2015 will encourage you to escape old patterns and opt to try new things. It is also a year that you may have to make a few big decisions. Make sure you follow your heart and stick to your own path.

Pisces

(February 20 – March 20)
You've been focused on perfecting particular aspects of your riding, and you might be thinking about competing this year. Whether you are aiming to go to your first show, or be part of a Pony Club team, be ambitious as your goals are within your reach!

With regards to a new pony, make sure you tell someone if you think something is wrong. Someone superior to you will thank you for it. Your intuition is very important in 2015.

Aries

(March 21 – April 20)
2015 holds some difficult decisions for you to make regarding your favourite pony. You know from experience that choosing an easy option can give unsatisfactory results. Patience is key. A decision made early in the year will be influential.

The first half of the year will see you being very particular about things, like learning a dressage test or keeping your tack clean, but remember that reward comes from details.

Taurus

(April 21 – May 21)
If something is working, don't change it, if not, don't panic! Remember not to push yourself or your pony too far this year, and don't get frustrated if you come across a situation which is out of your control. Stay relaxed, as you will always find a way to solve problems.

This year is all about having fun for those born under the sign of Taurus, so chill out and have a fab time with your fave pony!

Gemini

(May 22 – June 21)
You might feel under pressure for you and your pony to perform in 2015. Don't let people who have negative opinions affect you. Staying organised will help you, and will ensure you feel less flustered, so make sure you keep on top of your stable management chores.

You will start to feel more relaxed by September, as a busy summer draws to a close. Spending time with friends and lots of bonding with your favourite pony will be good for you this year.

Cancer

(June 22 – July 22)
For Cancer, 2015 is a year for self-discovery. You might find a new activity for you and your pony to enjoy, or uncover a talent you didn't know you had!

If you had a negative experience in 2014, like a bad fall or loss of confidence, remember to stay positive and look forward. Cancerians can be very emotional, just be sure not to bottle up your emotions, as it won't benefit you in the long run.

Horses

Check out what the future holds for you and your fave pony i

Leo

(July 23 – August 23)

Use your imagination in 2015! Leos are very creative people, just don't confuse dreams with reality. If you remember this, then anything is possible for you this year.

Follow a dream, try something you've always wanted to try and you're sure to be successful. Friendships are very important for you in 2015, and you should try to spend lots of time with family, too.

Virgo

(August 24 – September 22)

Virgo's tend to be quite critical, but it will help you to see the positive side of all situations in 2015. Learn lessons from mistakes and don't be too hard on yourself if you have a fall or a problem with your riding.

Keep your faith in yourself and your pony and you will be able to learn from any mishaps and turn them into positive experiences.

Libra

(September 23 – October 22)

You have a burden on your shoulders between May and August in 2015. Maybe you have a secret that you are unwilling to share, or you found out somebody else's secret. Trust your instincts and do the right thing.

Trust your friends to help you when you need it, and trust your pony when trying a new activity – you will make a great team in 2015.

Scorpio

(October 23 – November 21)

You will find new ways of doing things in 2015. Outdated and boring routines from last year will be a thing of the past. Try reorganising your grooming kit or your rug collection, and aim to keep them in order for the whole year.

Don't push issues or arguments with friends and family this year, as you may regret it. And have patience with a troublesome pony – he could surprise you!

Sagittarius

(November 22 – December 21)

Sagittarians are usually very optimistic and have the ability to see the bigger picture. Follow this instinct and don't get stuck in an unrewarding situation because you are worried about change. Ride a new pony, or enter a jumping class. Step outside your comfort zone in 2015.

Try to remain calm even if you don't achieve the goals you want to achieve. Avoid disappointment by reminding yourself what a great pony, family and friends you have!

Capricorn

(December 22 – January 20)

Someone superior to you is generous early in the year, but you may be offered something you have no need for. Keep your long-term needs in mind in 2015 and make careful choices.

2015 brings opportunities to stabilise aspects of your life. This could be new friends or a new pony! You feel very focused later in the year, so it could be a great time to have some schooling lessons or to perfect a dressage test.

FESS UPS!

DOUBLE BATH TIME!

Me and my friend Chloe were going to a show, so we gave our ponies a bath – then my friend's mobile rang from the feed room just as we were finishing. I offered to tie her pony up to the field fence to dry off with my pony. I put everything away and started to clean tack when Chloe returned to the yard and screamed at me. Her pony, Galen, had wriggled out of his headcollar and was rolling in the dust!

Of course, I got the blame – everyone knows Galen gets out of his headcollar unless it is securely fastened – and Chloe made me bath him again. Doh!

Jem

OH, VERY FUNNY...

MEGA EMBARRASSMENT!

GET OFF, I'LL DO IT!

I let my friend Polly ride my pony, Jet, and she wanted to jump. Jet's okay to jump, so I said yes, and Polly went over a few times. Then Jet decided she didn't have to jump after all (Polly's not a very experienced rider) and began to stop.

There were lots of other people schooling their ponies at the same time, and I knew Jet ought to end on a good note, so I told Polly to dismount, and I got on instead. Normally, Jet sails over everything, but she was obviously quite annoyed by this point and instead of jumping as usual, she put in a last-minute stop with me and I landed right up her neck, getting a mouthful of mane.

Everyone sniggered (cos I'd made a big thing about how I'd get Jet over easily), and I felt really stupid. I had to put the jump down to virtually a pole on the ground before Jet would go over it. I felt about the size of a pea....

Megan

MEGA EMBARRASSMENT!

HOSEPIPE BAN

One summer evening, when I turned my pony out at our DIY yard I noticed the trough was almost empty. Turning on the hose, I told myself I'd go back and turn it off when I'd done all my stable chores.

Only I forgot.

The next morning, the whole trough was surrounded by a huge flood – the hose had been going all night! The yard owner freaked out – and I was way too scared to admit it had been me who had left it running. Maybe they'll read this, and I'll feel better for having fessed up (or maybe they'll ban me from the yard!).

Tess

EPIC EMBARRASSMENT!

I AM SUCH A SHOWJUMPER... NOT!

HAVE YOU EVER SUFFERED AN EMBARRASSING INCIDENT AT THE STABLES? HERE ARE SOME CRINGES - ENJOY!

CLEAN-SWEEP

I was helping at the riding school and everyone was sweeping the yard. I lent my broom up against the wall for a second, while I took off my jumper, but when I reached for it, it had gone! Everyone thought I was just getting out of the work, but during evening stables later on, the broom turned up in Shadow's stable.

Shadow makes a habit of picking up brooms and dragging them over her door into her stable. The handle was all chewed so although everyone knew I'd been telling the truth, I still got told off for allowing a good broom to be ruined!

Sophie

OOOOH, I LOVE A BROOM, ME!

MEGA EMBARRASSMENT!

BARKING MAD!

When my mum came to collect me from the stables, she brought our Jack Russell, Jake, with her. He's very sharp, and as soon as she opened the car door, Jake rushed out to find me, charging off down to the indoor school. Unfortunately, there was a beginner lesson in there and as Jake dashed by, barking, all the ponies took off in different directions, like a box of fireworks. Nearly everyone fell off and the instructor gave me a right telling off in front of everyone, over the noise of her pupils wailing and crying. Like it was *my* fault!

Debs

EPIC EMBARRASSMENT!

GENTLY DOES IT

I was ever-so-gently riding my friend Helen's jumping pony, who had just recovered from lameness, and was under strict orders not to canter or jump her – so I didn't, obviously. Unfortunately, two other girls were jumping their ponies, and had put up several jumps in the outdoor school.

Dodging round them, I was just thinking of ending my ride and taking Jewel in when Helen arrived and shouted across to me. Looking over, I waved at her – but didn't realise Jewel was lined up and looking towards one of the jumps. Being the great jumping pony she is she went from a walk to canter and popped over it – right in front of her owner!

Once Helen calmed down she actually found it funny, and Jewel was no worse for wear. Thank goodness!

Samantha

IT WASN'T MY IDEA...

EPIC EMBARRASSMENT!

71

quiz!
Riding challenge

Are you an aids aficionado? Fully up-to-speed with paces? So not a diagonal dunce? Well find out with our riding quiz!

The aids (1)

Which of these are *natural* aids, and which are classed as *artificial* aids?

Whip   ....

Voice   ....

Seat   ....

Hands   ....

Spurs   ....

Legs   ....

The aids (2)

What are you asking your pony for if you...

1: ... sit up, feel on your inside rein, use your inside leg at the girth, and your outside leg behind the girth?

....

2: ... sit up, close your legs around your pony and your hands around the reins?

....

3: ... look left, bring your left shoulder and hip back, feel on your left rein, allow with the right rein, use your left leg at the girth and your right leg behind the girth?

....

Inside... outside...

When riding in a school or arena, the side of the pony and rider nearest the fence or wall is the *outside*. The side nearest the middle of the school is the *inside*.

1. Which rider leg asks for impulsion and encourages a pony to bend correctly?

☐ inside leg   ☐ outside leg

2. Which rider leg influences the pony's quarters?

☐ inside leg   ☐ outside leg

3. Which rider hand asks for direction?

☐ inside hand   ☐ outside hand

4. Which rider hand controls and regulates the pace, and controls the pony's bend?

☐ inside hand   ☐ outside hand

Pace yourself...

How many beats to each stride in:

Walk ....

Trot ....

Canter ....

Gallop ....

What is another word for impulsion?

☐ Energy ☐ Speed ☐ Action

Which of these are real and which are not real paces?

Extended walk ☐ real ☐ not real

Working trot ☐ real ☐ not real

Collected walk ☐ real ☐ not real

Medium canter ☐ real ☐ not real

Counter trot ☐ real ☐ not real

Extended canter ☐ real ☐ not real

Short trot ☐ real ☐ not real

Counter canter ☐ real ☐ not real

Diagonal dilemma!

Diagonals – everyone gets confused with their trot diagonals! How many of these are correct?

1: When rising to the trot on the left rein, the rider should be sitting as the pony's right foreleg is on the ground.

☐ true ☐ false

2: When rising to the trot on the left rein, the rider should be sitting as the pony's left foreleg is on the ground.

☐ true ☐ false

3: To change diagonal as you change the rein, the rider sits for a single beat in the middle of the change – usually at X.

☐ true ☐ false

Getting fancy!

What movement is this describing?

The rider halts next to the wall and asks the pony to move his hindquarters around his pivoting front hooves until he is facing the opposite direction.

....

Which of these statements correctly describe lateral movements?

1. The horse or pony moves forward and sideways

2. The horse or pony's forelegs and hind legs move on different tracks

3. The horse or pony hops away from the rider's leg

4. The horse or pony is trained to move away from the rider's leg.

How did you do? Turn to page 98 for the answers!

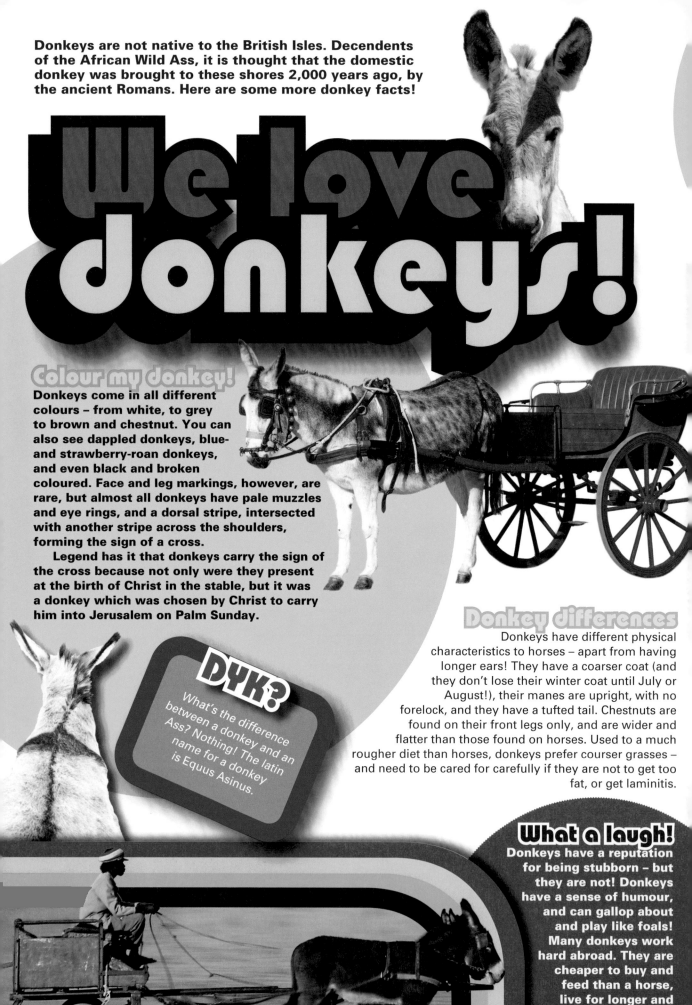

Donkeys are not native to the British Isles. Decendents of the African Wild Ass, it is thought that the domestic donkey was brought to these shores 2,000 years ago, by the ancient Romans. Here are some more donkey facts!

We love donkeys!

Colour my donkey!

Donkeys come in all different colours – from white, to grey to brown and chestnut. You can also see dappled donkeys, blue- and strawberry-roan donkeys, and even black and broken coloured. Face and leg markings, however, are rare, but almost all donkeys have pale muzzles and eye rings, and a dorsal stripe, intersected with another stripe across the shoulders, forming the sign of a cross.

Legend has it that donkeys carry the sign of the cross because not only were they present at the birth of Christ in the stable, but it was a donkey which was chosen by Christ to carry him into Jerusalem on Palm Sunday.

DYK?

What's the difference between a donkey and an Ass? Nothing! The latin name for a donkey is Equus Asinus.

Donkey differences

Donkeys have different physical characteristics to horses – apart from having longer ears! They have a coarser coat (and they don't lose their winter coat until July or August!), their manes are upright, with no forelock, and they have a tufted tail. Chestnuts are found on their front legs only, and are wider and flatter than those found on horses. Used to a much rougher diet than horses, donkeys prefer courser grasses – and need to be cared for carefully if they are not to get too fat, or get laminitis.

What a laugh!

Donkeys have a reputation for being stubborn – but they are not! Donkeys have a sense of humour, and can gallop about and play like foals! Many donkeys work hard abroad. They are cheaper to buy and feed than a horse, live for longer and complain less. Poor donkeys!

Hee-haw!

Unlike horses, donkeys bray to each other instead of neighing. It is very loud, and can be heard for miles!

Meet the rels!

There are wild donkeys living abroad and in zoos – and here are some of them:

The Kiang

This fluffy-looking ass lives wild in the Tibetan Plateau and can grow up to 13.3hh. Red in colour with a thick dorsal stripe, their main predator is the wolf. But when wolves strike, the Kiangs form a circle, kicking out at them!

The Onager

This amazingly fast ass lives in Asia and Mongolia and has been reintroduced into the Ukraine, Israel, Uzbekistan and Kazakstan. These endangered asses are very fast and notoriously untamable! The good news is that they are breeding in captivity.

The Somalia Wild Ass

No prizes for guessing that this ass comes from Somali! Famous for its beautiful leg stripes, they are critically endangered – fewer than 1000 now live in the wild. Luckily, these amazing asses are breeding in captivity.

Visit the Donkey Breed Society website (wwwdonkeybreedsociety. co.uk) to find out more about donkeys, and to see what they can do!

BAD WEATHER?
NO PROBLEM!

WE ALL LOVE RIDING AS MUCH AS WE CAN. HERE'S HOW TO PREVENT BAD WEATHER GETTING IN THE WAY!

RAIN, RAIN, GO AWAY

The winter months in particular can gift us with many rainy days and washed-out weekends, but don't let it stop you riding your fave pony. Get yourself kitted out with rain-repelling gear so it doesn't spoil your fun!

HERE'S WHAT YOU NEED TO GO RIDING IN THE RAIN:

FOR YOU:
● Waterproof jacket
● Waterproof trousers (especially in heavy rain)

FOR YOUR PONY:
● Ride-on rain sheet

AFTER YOUR RIDE:
Make sure that the parts of your pony that did get wet are dried off with a towel, and that he is left to dry off in a stable with a sweat or wicking rug on. Don't put a turnout rug on him and put him back out in the field until he has dried off completely and is warm. Make sure you get warm as well!

WHITE OUT?

Riding in the snow is a bit more tricky for a number of reasons. Firstly, snow can cover icy patches of ground which are very dangerous for ponies. In light snow it is a better option to ride in an arena, where you know the ground is safe. It is not safe to ride in heavy snow, as vision could be impaired and ponies hooves could become impacted.

HERE'S WHAT YOU WILL NEED FOR RIDING IN THE SNOW:

FOR YOU:
● Very warm clothes and boots!
● Gloves
● Waterproof jacket

FOR YOUR PONY:
● A ride-on fleece or waterproof exercise rug

AFTER YOUR RIDE:
Snow can sometimes make ponies damp as snowflakes land on them and melt. Make sure you dry your pony off thoroughly before putting a turnout rug on him, and pick out his hooves thoroughly to remove any ice.

FOG BOTHER

Riding in the early morning during the winter can mean braving foggy conditions. The most important thing to think about when riding in fog is how well you can see and how well you can *be seen*. Do not ride on roads when it is foggy.

HERE'S WHAT YOU WILL NEED FOR RIDING IN FOG:

FOR YOU:
● Reflective jacket or reflective tabard

FOR YOUR PONY:
● Reflective items such as boots, neckstrap or bridle covers
● A reflective ride-on rug if it is very cold

AFTER YOUR RIDE:
Providing it wasn't raining and your pony didn't get wet, your pony can be turned out or stabled in approprite rugs (if he wears one) after your ride. Take care in foggy conditions leading your pony to his field, especially if it is not adjacent to the yard. Make sure you keep your reflective jacket or tabard on so others can still see you.

TOP TIP!

When the weather is very cold, while grooming your pony before and after riding keep his rug on and fold one half back to groom his neck and shoulders, then fold the other half forward to groom his body. Don't leave your pony standing around with no rug on, particularly if he is fully clipped.

WHEN IS IT NOT SAFE TO RIDE?

HIGH WINDS. High winds can present some problems when it comes to riding. Ponies can become spooky and skittish when it is very windy. Also, objects might blow around and the wind can cause some strange noises which might frighten ponies.

HEAVY SNOW. Heavy snow is a problem because as it falls it makes visibility very poor. If it is already deep it will be hard for ponies to walk through, and their hooves could become packed with ice.

ICY CONDITIONS. Icy conditions might be likely on winter mornings. It is sensible to wait until later in the day to ride when ice has had a chance to thaw. Avoid riding on roads and be aware that arenas may be frozen solid. Take care on concrete yards as horses (and humans) may slip on icy patches.

VERY HEAVY RAIN. Riding your pony when it is raining heavily could unsettle or spook him and put you in an unsafe situation. It is also likely to make the ground underfoot very slippery, which can be dangerous. There is also a likelihood of lightning and flooding.

Charlie goes Disco Dancing!

The hardest decision of my life

Isabelle found it hard to say goodbye to her old friend...

Splash was my oldest – and very much my best – friend. She came into my life when I was only nine and now I'm in my third year at Uni. Splash had been quite old when I first got her – although nobody knew exactly how old. She had been game, though, and together we'd seen Pony Club camps, won almost 400 rosettes and done just about everything a girl and a pony could do together. We'd been a formidable team!

SPLASH THE STAR

Later, though, when I retired Splash in the field with other ponies, I chatted to her in the field, or I sat and read to her – Splash had always loved being read to. I made sure all her jabs were up-to-date, and I booked the dentist twice a year to keep her teeth in good order, repaying her back for the good times we'd had together.

But then I noticed how Splash took longer to come to the gate when I arrived every evening to feed her.

We'd been a formidable team!

She was no longer the lively pony who had raced to victory in bending races, the pony who won Chase-me-Charlies. I remembered how we had been picked for our Pony Club jumping team, and Splash had clinched the title for us with a fantastic clear round. She'd been a total star – everyone knew her from her bright pink saddle cloth. It had been her trademark. I always had pink accessories for her – even though pink clashed with her chestnut coat!

A SHOULDER TO CRY ON

But it hadn't just been about winning rosettes or being picked for teams. Splash had always been there for me whenever I'd had a crisis in my life. When I fell in love with Danny Proctor, and he cheated on me with Alexa Smith at the school prom, Splash had stood patiently as I wept into her chestnut mane, and had nuzzled my shoulder as if to say, "Cheer up Bella, you've still got me. Who needs boys?"

Splash had been there for me when my nana died, and I didn't know who to talk to about how I felt. She'd listened to all my stories about how Nana and I had enjoyed a great bond. And, of course, when I fretted and worried about my school grades and exam results, we rode out for long rides which made me forget my troubles for a while – and my worries had been unfounded because my grades and results had been fine!

TIME MARCHES ON

Splash got slower, and thinner, despite all my care, and I tried not to notice how her hips stuck out, and how long it took her to get up after enjoying a sleep in the field. The other ponies had no respect for my friend,

chasing her away from the piles of hay we put out. I put her hay at a distance from them, and stood over her as she munched on soaked pony cubes, the mash dropping from her mouth as her teeth, despite care, wore down.

Splash was getting old. I couldn't bear it, I refused to face it. I told myself she was fine, that she was happy in her retirement. I couldn't imagine life without my pony Splash.

Splash had always been there for me whenever I'd had a crisis in my life

A DEEP SIGH

Then, one summer day, I went to sit with her in the field as I often did. I loved watching her graze, remembering the good times, reliving our successes and special moments. Only this day was different. On this day Splash came and put her muzzle on my shoulder and I heard her give a deep, deep sigh. Splash was sad, so sad, and I realised that she was trying to tell me something.

"What is it, old girl," I asked, stroking her nose. But I knew what Splash was trying to say. It was time. However much I hated to face it, I had to do the last kindness for my old friend. With tears streaming down my face I pulled out my mobile and dialled

I told Splash how much I loved her...

the vet's number and as we both waited for him to arrive I told Splash how much I loved her, and how she had been the best pony anyone could ever wish for, and how terribly I would miss her. I was a total wreck.

NEVER FORGOTTEN

I had Splash cremated – her ashes are buried in our garden, a cherry tree planted above. Every spring the deep pink blossoms which remind me of my perfect pony swirl around Splash's final resting place. She'll never be forgotten, my beautiful, wonderful pony, Splash.

I loved spending time with Splash

posed by models

English ponies!

Dartmoor

The small but beautifully formed Dartmoor pony is an elegant children's riding pony with a good action. Popular in Europe, the Belgians even race them!

Dartmoor facts

- Height: up to 12.2hh
- Any coat colour except piebald and skewbald
- Evidence on the moors proves that ponies were to be found there 3,500 years ago!
- The Dartmoor pony is considered *Vulnerable* (between 500-900 left) by the Rare Breeds Survival Trust.

England boasts no fewer than five ponies native to its shores. Not only do they have a fascinating history, but you can still see three English breeds roaming ancient moors and forests today!

New Forest

Native to the New Forest National Park in Hampshire, Southern England. Visitors to the New Forest delight in seeing the ponies roaming free. All are owned, however, and there are regular roundups where ponies are caught and either sold or re-released into the Forest.

New Forest facts

- Height: Between 12.2hh and 14.2hh
- Any coat colour except piebald and skewbald
- As with most of Britain's natives, the small ponies seen roaming the Forest bear little resemblence to the quality New Forest ponies bred on the studs. They make great mounts for adults and children.

Exmoor

The Exmoor is one of the oldest breeds in the world. It has a distinctive jaw formation and the beginings of a seventh molar, found in no other equine. It is always the distinct Exmoor colour, with a mealy muzzle and toad eye.

Native to Exmoor for centuries, evidence of these ponies goes back to the Bronze Age – Exmoor ponies would have pulled Queen Boudicea's chariot!

Exmoor facts

- Height: Between 12.2hh – 12.3hh
- Britain's oldest breed of native pony
- Coat colour: Various shades of bay, brown and dun. No white markings are allowed. At all!
- The Exmoor pony is considered *Endangered* (between only 300-500) by the Rare Breeds Survival Trust.

Fell

These ponies used to roam the northern Fells of England in what is now Cumbria. Once known as Galloways, the people of Cumberland would pit their ponies against each other in trotting races and today's Fell ponies are still famous for their ability to trot well. Used extensively as pack ponies, they used to carry virtually anything – the ancient equine equivalent of a long-distance lorry!

Fell facts

- Max height: 14hh
- Fells are popular with the British Monarchy as ride-and-drive ponies
- Coat colour: Black, bay and grey, – the only white markings allowed being a small star
- The Fell pony is considered *At Risk* (between only 900-1500) by the Rare Breeds Survival Trust.

Dales

The Dales pony is England's biggest native pony, standing up to 14.2hh with a cobby build – a real powerhouse! They are native to the upper dales – from the Scottish border to the High Peaks of Derbyshire. These strong ponies were used for packing and could carry a load of 240lbs for 100 miles a week! They are ideal for riding or driving.

Dales facts

- Max height: 14.2hh
- Their breed combines stamina and courage with a calm temperament
- Coat colours: Black, brown, bay and sometimes grey. Roan is occasionally seen. The only white markings allowed are a star and/or a snip and white to the hind fetlocks.
- The Dales pony is considered *Endangered* (between only 300-500) by the Rare Breeds Survival Trust.

Dreams of a Pony

How a pony in the night changed the life of a maid

PONY short story winner!

By Jamilah Ranger

There was something different about today. I could feel it. I even swept the floor with such energy this morning, I almost knocked the Lord of the Manor over! You see, it all started last night. I had been lying on my straw mattress, contemplating how strange it was that straw was comfortable to horses, yet could be so horrible for humans, when something caught my attention.

Let me explain a few things about myself. I am a simple maid for the Manor House at the top of the village. Of course, I would never be allowed on horseback – that is for the gentry or tradesmen. Unfortunately, I am infatuated with horses and ponies, and I just can't seem to change the way I feel. Every so often, when I'm sent to the orchard to pick apples or tend to the trees, I'll climb a tree and watch the grooms at work. Or perhaps, when tasked to dust the shelves in the library, I will spend a particularly long time in the equine area, reading up on every detail of how to care for horses (some of which can't be right, but 19th century medicine is hardly what I would call completely trustworthy).

Anyhow, last night I was, as usual, engrossed in thoughts of horses, when I was startled out of my daze by a noise. I lay there, just listening for another sound, another hint of what could be happening, when I heard what could only be described as an agitated whinny. I leapt to my feet and darted nimbly across to the window, drawing back the linen strips which acted as curtains. To my surprise, even though it was perhaps about three in the morning and the stables

There were rumours of beasts in the forest...

The beast snorted and I could feel its warm breath on the back of my neck

were on the other side of the estate, there was a group of grooms struggling to recapture what looked like a small (I'm guessing about 14.2hh) gelding. It looked well toned, and its dark coat shone in the silvery moonlight of the night.

Odd, I thought. The Lord of the Manor really preferred large hunter stallions that were sleek and athletic, not small, jumpy geldings. I was about to return to bed when the gelding gave one last frustrated kick and bolted for the fir forest. I shuffled uneasily. There were rumours of beasts in there and even though I wasn't sure if I believed them or not, I couldn't bear the thought of leaving a poor, frightened pony alone somewhere like that, especially as the grooms gave up and headed towards their quarters.

Suddenly, an idea hit me. It was an idea so risky, so ridiculous, I should have expelled it from my head immediately. But my heart began to pound and, as I felt the blood coursing through my veins, I took a deep, calming breath. I couldn't just be a boring maid all my life! I had to make my life worth something, add a few twists. And so I decided: I was going to sneak out and search for the pony.

It was cold outside and a spring frost coated the grass. I shivered as I pulled my thin shawl around my shoulders. It was just as I reached the edge of the courtyard that a thought occurred to me; the pony's lead rope was slung over the fence and I realised I would need it if I intended to catch the poor thing. If I *could* catch it, that was. I stole over the grass and was soon faced with the ominous, dark treeline of the forest. It was truly terrifying, I can tell you!

After about five minutes of walking between darting shadows and rustling leaves, a sound caught my attention. There was something behind me, and it sounded big. I froze, not daring to turn around and face my worst fears. The beast snorted and I could feel its warm breath on the back of my neck. My adrenalin kicked in and I ran as fast as I possibly could, heading deeper into the forest with every step I took. Eventually, my legs began to slow to a halt and my lungs burned as if they were on fire. I sank to the ground, nervous and shaking.

I jumped as something touched my back and as I began to turn my head to get one, final look at the beast, I heard a soft whinny of delight. I swung around and when the sight of the beast that had been chasing me met my eyes, I began to laugh – in fact, I couldn't stop! How could I have been so silly? I had been chased by the runaway pony who had, in fact, just wanted to say hello! I wrapped my arms around his neck and buried my face into his mane. He nuzzled my shoulder again and I looked into his big, soft, brown eyes. I patted him and whispered words of comfort as I tied the rope onto his head collar.

As I lead him back along the path, I realised that the danger wasn't over yet. There were many paths in the forest, and the tall fir trees blotted out most of the moonlight. I knew that I'd be fine if I stuck to the paths, but I vaguely remembered passing a couple of crossings and it wasn't long before I reached one of these. I only managed to find my way back by glancing at the ground every so often, and looking for hoof prints or my own footprints.

When we did, eventually, reach the Manor again, I tied the pony to the fencing and sprinted to the hay barn. Grabbing a spare haynet, I also tied that to the fence. The stables were too far away to take the pony there now. I gave him one last hug and returned to my quarters where I promptly fell into a dreamy sleep.

And that is where we started. There was something different about today. Word had reached practically every servant in the household. A runaway pony that nobody thought would be found had mysteriously appeared in the courtyard with a haynet and no injuries whatsoever. Everybody had ruled out any of the grooms being involved, as they would have almost certainly returned the pony to a nice, warm stable. But who could it have been?

Hushed whispers and glances were being exchanged left, right and centre, and one rumour reached my ears that His Lordship had gone mad and was seen attempting to ride the pony bareback along the hill. Only I knew what had really happened.

I was once again 'dusting' the shelves in the library when the servant bell rang out. Jumping down from my little perch, I slid *The Perfect Guide to Stable Management* back into its place. The servant bell is what Arabella, Lady of the Manor rings when she needs to talk to any of the staff. There are different bells for maids, cooks, butlers and general boys. Today it was for the maids, which meant me. I hurried to the kitchen and took my place in the line. Her Ladyship looked very serious, and asked us all to sit down.

"Now," she said, "I am sure you are all aware of the events that took place last night. We have reason to believe that the rescuer of the pony was a maid, judging by the footprints left in the forest – they were made by a maid's shoes. I would like the person amongst you who was involved to step forward and admit to it."

I swallowed. This was bad, very bad. I just couldn't decide what to do. I would be found out eventually, and I knew it, too. Surely it was better to admit it now and beg for forgiveness? Or maybe I wouldn't be discovered, and should wait. Just as I decided to keep quiet, Her Ladyship's face softened. She smiled.

"Nothing bad will happen to you, I promise. Please do not be afraid to come forward and tell us – you have done a good deed! Without you, that pony may not have survived. We owe you our gratitude."

This was it, I knew what I had to do. Taking a deep breath I stepped forward and muttered, "It was me, Ma'am."

"Thank you, Milly," said Her Ladyship. "Please follow me."

I knew I had no choice but to do as I was told, so I stepped down the corridor behind her, towards His Lordship's study.

Lady Arabella rapped sharply on the door.

"Enter!" came the reply. Her Ladyship pushed the door open and I shuffled in after her. It wasn't long before I had explained all that had happened the night before – and would you believe it, His Lordship began laughing uncontrollably when I told of how I realised it was the pony which had been chasing me.

"Well," he said, "it seems you have had quite an adventure. We are truly grateful. Aurora belonged to my dear cousin, but she lost interest in riding and we offered to keep him. We didn't intend to ride him, though, and he isn't the driving sort, so I was at rather a loose end as to what we could do with the poor creature. We seem to have found our solution, though! What you did last night was valiant and brave and, as it happens, I have heard from the grooms and other maids of your interest in and love of horses. Would you, Milly, be willing to care for, ride and be wholly responsible for Aurora?"

"Yes! Yes! Oh thank you Sir, thank you! I would be delighted, you are so kind!" I said, the words escaping from my mouth in an excited flurry.

"It is my pleasure," said His Lordship. "Of course, you would be relieved of your household duties and have to help the grooms in your spare time. Now go. Pack your things and find a spare room in the groom's quarters. Aurora will be waiting in the stables," he commanded, a beaming smile breaking across his face.

And that is how I went from being a mere unnoticed maid to caring for my own wonderful bay pony. I am the happiest girl in the world at the moment, and even our own Queen Victoria could not have had a more wonderful childhood. All the riches in the world couldn't buy my happiness!

"I have heard from the grooms and other maids of your love of horses"

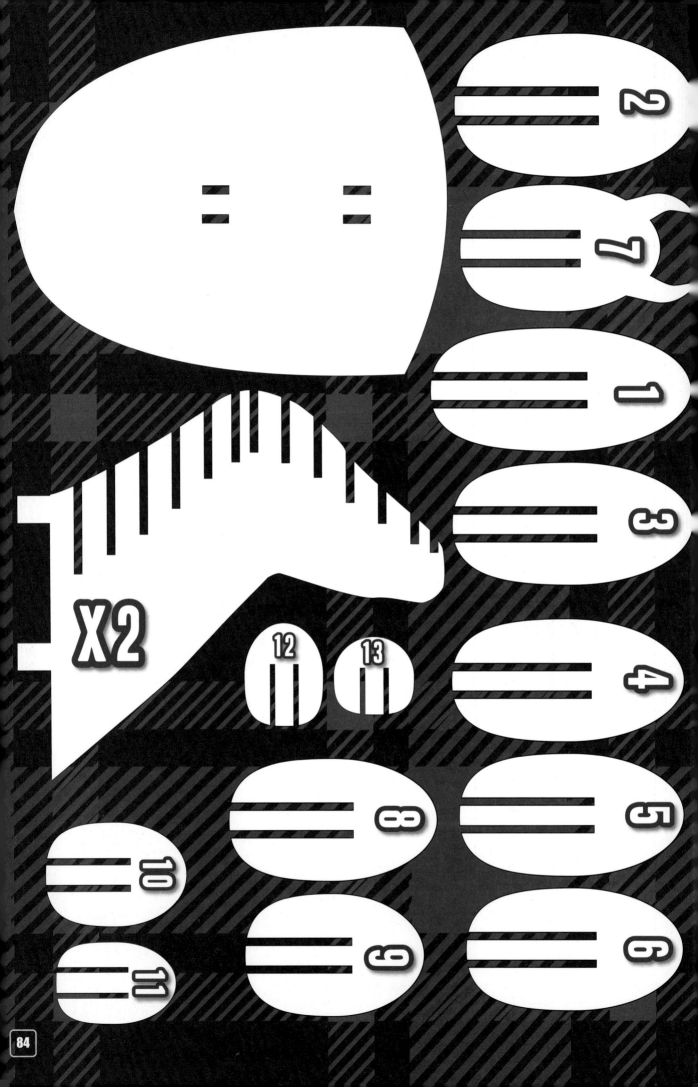

Make a horse head decoration!

Stag's heads are *soooo* yesterday. Make yourself a brilliant 3D horse head to put on your wall!

HOW TO DO IT

1. Scan our pattern on this page (or trace it onto tracing paper). You will need all the pieces – but you can scale it up to make your horse head as big as you want. The bigger the horse, the thicker the cardboard you will need.

2. Print your pattern, then trace it onto the cardboard you are using. Go a bit wild – we've used black sparkly card for the horse, and given him a gold mane! Try different colours, or a flowery cardboard pattern, for a modern look. Glue your cardboard together so that both sides are patterned. Why not make more than one horse head?

3. Carefully cut all the pieces out – and cut the slots, too. You will need two head and neck pieces.

4. Now assemble your horse head. It is pretty simple to see which parts go where, and we've numbered them for you to make sure they go in the right order, starting from the back. Add the mane and slot the neck onto the shield, taping it on the wrong side to keep it in place.

5. Now hang your horse head on the wall and enjoy!

You will need

- The pattern on this page
- Some stiff cardboard
- Scissors
- Glue

That's it!

My week as a cowgirl!

Ruby and her parents had the best holiday ever when they stayed on an American ranch!

When my parents told me we were going on a ranch holiday in the USA I screamed with joy! I couldn't believe it – I was so excited! We all rode at our local riding school, my parents and me, and Mum and Dad thought it would be a terrific way to spend a holiday. I could hardly wait.

When we arrived at the Double W Ranch in Montana we'd been travelling through the most amazing, sweeping countryside for what seemed like an age. Owners Bud and Marsha greeted us and introduced us to all the other holiday makers. I was the only teenager!

MEET COMANCHE!

The next day, after a fantastic barbeque and a great night in our own log cabin, it was time to meet our horses. Mum was given a beautiful palomino mare called Whisper, and Dad had an Appalooosa gelding with wall eyes called Bobby Joe. Me, I was handed the reins of the most stunning paint pony I'd ever seen.

"Comanche's a peach to ride and a real honey to care for!" said Marsha

"Ruby, meet Comanche," drawled Marsha. "He's a peach to ride and a real honey to care for. You'll both get on real swell, I know it!"

And we did. As soon as I sat in Comanche's big western saddle I felt at home. The horn at the front felt strange, but the saddle was comfortable, and Comanche had a beautiful bridle decorated with silver. Instead of a browband he had a loop around each ear, and the reins, rather than being joined together were split, so I daren't drop them.

"Just lean those reins against his neck to turn him," explained Marsha, mounting her own buckskin called Shady Lady, and leading us out onto the prarie.

COW SENSE

We rode out and helped with the cattle, herding them together, rounding them up and helping with the branding. I hated seeing the young cattle being branded, but the ranch was so vast, there was no other way to keep track of which cattle belonged to which rancher. Comanche looked after me – he set off after strays even before I had noticed them. He had what Bud called *cow sense*.

"He's gotta lotta Quarter Horse in him," Bud explained, "and they're born cattle horses. He'll look after you, that savvy paint cow pony!"

And he did. At the end of the day I slid out of Comanche's saddle tired but happy. We still had the horses to care for, but we didn't mind. It was the least we could do to thank them for carrying us over the ranch all day.

LIFE ON THE TRAIL

In the days that followed we rode out and tended cattle – driving a herd from one pasture to another one day, and riding a trail to a brilliant campsite another where we stayed overnight, the horses tied to a rope slung between two trees. It was so cool being able to sneak up to Comanche before going to bed in my sleeping bag, and sharing some bread from dinner. Mum and Dad were enjoying themselves too – it was a million miles away from riding at the riding school.

I slid out of Comanche's saddle tired but happy

TEARS ON MY PILLOW

The end of our holiday came far too quickly. Our last day was spent at a local rodeo and although it was brilliant, I missed Comanche. I didn't want to leave my gorgeous paint pony and I cried into my pillow on the last night. Mum and Dad were just as upset at leaving their mounts, too – Mum even shed a tear and Dad sniffed a bit. We were all a bit quiet on the way home. We agreed it had been the best holiday we had ever, *ever* had, and that we would definitely go back!

WE'RE GETTING A HORSE!

We're back home now, and back to riding at the riding school, but our ranch holiday made Mum and Dad decide to get a family horse. I can't wait! But I'll never forget Comanche, my lovely paint pony who turned me into a cowgirl for a week!

Me and Comanche

posed by models

WHO'S THAT CELEB?

Think you know your celebrity riders? You might do, but we've made it a bit tricky for you with some sneaky cover-ups and unusual angles. They're well tricky!

WHO'S WHO?

We're on familiar ground here. Can you spot the riders in the saddles?

1

6

8

7

10

11

3

5

9

2

4

DOGGONE IT!

All celeb riders have dogs – fact! But can you name these famous riders, pictured with their faithful hounds?

A

B

C

D

E

F

TEACHER, TEACHER

They all teach, our celeb riders, but can you recognise them when they're doing it? (They're the ones on the ground!)

1
....

2
....

3
....

4
....

5
....

6
....

....
....
....

7

8
....

A
....

B
....
....

C
....

RIDERS AT HOME

Who are these famous riders in unfamiliar roles?

D

E

F

TURN TO PAGE 98 FOR THE ANSWERS!

Part 2

Duggie has been finding messages about himself written in stones in the field. He believes they're a sign.

Help me find message six.

Is this it? With six on it?

Oh the suspense!

There could be hundreds of these things...

'DUGGIE IS A PONY WHO IS ...

You don't want to see this.

That's right, nothing to see here.

It says something important, doesn't it?

No, no, not at all.

Nothing you'll want to read.

SNIGGER

PHWWWAHHHH!

It was you two, all along, wasn't it! Very funny.

Spring

Spring can be a tricky time for rugging ponies, as the weather can be quite warm but with rain showers. The best type of rug to use would be a rainsheet to turnout in – which is the equivalent to a human wearing a rain coat! A light stable rug with around 100-150g of filling will do the job for a chilly night in a stable.

Rugging ponies can be
or too cold? With th
your pony is *juuuuust* righ

- No fill or 100g light fill
- Tough outer shell and breathable lining
- **Keeps rain off pony's back**
- Adds a layer for some warmth

Think! Does your pony need a rug at all? Only rug if necessary!

Summer

During the summer months, most ponies will be turned out without a rug on. Ponies love this as they can roll and scratch with their friends without rugs getting in the way! However, ponies may wear fly rugs during the summer. These are lightweight rugs with very fine mesh which stop horses getting bothered by flies landing on them.

In the stable, they can wear a stable sheet, which can also be particularly handy to use before a show, as it helps keep the dust off and prevent stable stains.

Rug fea

- **Standard cut rugs.** These are simple shape rugs that do not have inbuilt neck pieces.

- **Neck pieces.** These attach to rugs of a standard shape. They offer extra protection by covering the pony's neck.

- **Combo rugs.** These are rugs with built-in neck pieces.

- **Half neck rug.** These rugs have a high-cut neck for extra protection.

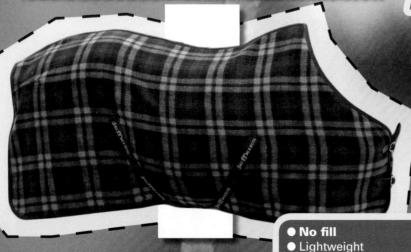

- **No fill**
- **Lightweight**
- **Keeps ponies clean**

g for asons

...inefield – is he too hot
...eature you can make sure
...rough every season!

Autumn

The autumn months, like spring, can also be tricky for rugging. Even if the sun is out, it can still be cold and it can be very wet. A good option is a medium weight rug which will be warm but is not as heavy as a thick, winter rug.

However, it may still be warm in autumn months, in which case, a lightweight turnout might be a better option on warmer days to prevent the pony from getting too hot and sweating.

For the stable, a rug with around 200g fill is often the best option. Keep in mind ponies may be clipped at this time of year and need something heavier at night.

- 200-250g fill
- **Medium weight**
- Adds insulation for extra warmth

Winter

- 370–450g fill
- **Heavyweight**
- Super-warm for winter months
- **Under rug (sometimes necessary for ponies who are clipped)**

Winter generally means cold, rain and sometimes snow. Most ponies will need heavy winter rugs. These usually have around 370-450g of fill, but some can have more. Fully clipped ponies may need a very heavy rug or a heavy rug and an under rug for extra warmth. You might want to add a neck piece to your pony's rug if it doesn't have one built-in.

Ponies stabled at night will need heavy stable rugs as, although they are indoors, they cannot move around much to keep warm like ponies who live out.

...tures

- **Leg arches**. A leg arch is shaping of the fabric around the tops of the legs that allows more movement.

- **Leg straps.** Straps that cross over between the pony's hind legs, and keep a turnout rug in place.

- **Fastenings.** Some rugs have trigger clips and others have buckles. There are usually fewer fastenings on stable rugs than on turnout rugs.

- **Tail flap**. Covers the top section of the tail to prevent wind and rain going between a pony's hind legs. Vital for pulled tails.

When we're not riding or caring for horses and ponies, we all love drawing them! We've tracked down some arty ways of depicting horses – why not try some yourself and send them to us at PONY Mag?

Make some pony bunting!

How fab are these stylised ponies? Can you find *your* own unique style?

Great use of colour and shape!

Why stick with paint when there are vegetables around?

Experiment with black and white!

HORSES!

Take one shape...

Don't forget sculpture! This fantastic sculpture, *The Heavy Horse* by Andy Scott, is next to the M8 motorway in Scotland. Made from steel bars, it stands 4.5 metres tall!

Pic: Matthi/Shutterstock.com

... and play with it!

Use a fave piece of fabric!

Take photographs inspired by Stubbs!

Pic: Sue Westwood-Ruttledge

Use of geometric shapes give this horse a 3D effect

95

Jorja's Journal

"You know what we need?" asked Matt, a blade of rye grass between his teeth.

"Chocolate!" cried Angelina, sitting up and fishing around in her pockets for some.

"No, not chocolate..." groaned Matt, faintly irritated.

"I disagree," said Molly.

"... an *adventure!*" said Matt. "*That's* what we need!"

We were all lying at the top of the hill, looking down at the ponies grazing in the adjoining field. At least, we *had* been looking down at the ponies, but it had got so hot we had all felt sleepy and had laid down in a row on the grass, looking up at the sky. The summer holidays stetched ahead of us and Matt, Molly, Angelina and I were feeling chilled. It's one of the best feelings in the world, knowing the next six weeks were going to be filled with nothing but ponies, ponies, ponies.

"Oh no, all my chocolate buttons have melted into one massive big blob," wailed Angelina.

"Yes, an adventure..." murmured Matt again, obviously annoyed.

"What, like finding stolen ponies, or sunken treasure, or rescuing someone stuck down a well?" I asked. It seemed unlikely.

"I was thinking more like a pony trek or something..." began Matt.

Molly and I sat up. That did sound like a good idea. "Go on," said Molly.

> *'An adventure!' said Matt. 'That's what we need!'*

"Oh, I've got melted chocolate in my hair!" groaned Angelina, sucking it off.

"We could ride the ponies along the bridleways in a big circle for three days," said Matt.

"And what would we do at night?" I asked, knowing already my parents wouldn't entertain it.

"Camp," said Matt. We could tether the ponies and camp out."

"We wouldn't be allowed," said Molly.

"We would if a grown-up came with us or, even better, just met us and stayed with us overnight," Matt said.

"You've obviously given this some thought," said Angelina, sucking chocolate off her fingers.

"Yeah, well, no good suggesting something unless you can follow it through," said Matt, a bit smugly.

"I vote we put it to our folks!" said Molly.

So we did. And guess what? They said yes! Molly's dad said he'd meet us for the two nights with two tents, and Angelina's mum made enquires about fields and friendly pony people who would let us camp in them and before we knew it we were getting ready to set off. Angelina was loaning a grey gelding with a black mane and tail called Puffin for the holidays, so she was up for it, and we set off from Marsh Farm three days later, the sun shining, the ponies keen and all of us excited beyond belief.

"We just follow the bridlepaths," Matt told us, confidently. "I've got a map and I'm pretty good at reading it, actually!"

"If you do say so yourself!" mumbled Molly. I gave Jigsaw's neck a rub. She seemed keen to follow Star along the bridlepath – it was one we rarely used as it just ran in a straight line, which meant we had to turn around and come back the same way, rather than ride in a loop. But not today! Matt was leading, Angelina was behind, then Molly, then me. I quite like being last. I can whisper and talk to Jigsaw without anyone (Matt!) teasing me. We rode for a couple of hours – enjoying several canters –

before dismounting and loosening the girths for a while to give the ponies a break. I took Jigsaw's bridle off (she was wearing her headcollar underneath) so she could graze for 10 minutes. We all had some sandwiches and cartons of drinks in our backpacks, so we tucked in.

"Where do we go now?" I asked Matt, who was busying himself with the map in an important fashion.

"Well, we have to go south-west," he told me, studying the symbols and then peering through the trees.

"Continue on the bridlepath, you mean?" asked Molly, sarcastically.

"Yeah, all right!" groaned Matt.

> *It was about five o'clock when we arrived at our first overnight stop*

We headed south-west (apparently), and the path widened so we could all ride abreast. Star kept threatening Puffin because he didn't know him, and poor Puffin kept stopping and running backwards, unaware that Star is a total wuss, and only does it when he knows Molly will prevent him from actually carrying out his threats.

The flies were horrible. The ponies had started to sweat in the heat and we'd forgotten to bring any repellent with us. Jigsaw began to shake her head, and twice she stopped dead to rub her eyes on her knees. I almost got pinged off over her shoulder.

"Come on, let's outrun them!" suggested Angelina, urging Puffin into a canter. We were in a wood and the ground underneath us was damp and soft, so we all cantered along, leaving the flies behind. Of course, it was only temporary, but it helped for a while.

It was about five o'clock when we arrived at our first overnight stop. I was glad to slide off Jigsaw – it had been a long day. Molly's dad had brought along his barbeque in the trailer, as well as our sleeping bags, tents and clean clothes. The field was full of trees so we tied the ponies to string around the trunks (because our ponies didn't know Puffin, we couldn't turn them out), before collapsing on the ground.

"Come on!" scolded Molly's dad, "you've got to groom your ponies and clean your tack before you eat, AND put up the tents!" Everyone groaned and Matt actually looked a bit sick. He never cleans tack – but he didn't mind brushing the sweat off CP and sponging him around his eyes and nose before fitting him with his fly mask. Then we put up our tents, which took a bit of doing as Molly's dad was the only one who knew how to do it, so it was quite late by the time we got to eat.

Molly's dad dished up sausages, burgers, jacket potatoes and beans, a real cowboy supper. And there was fresh fruit for afters, and tons of fizzy water. I went to say goodnight to Jiggy, who had eaten all the grass around her tree, so I fetched a haynet for her. It was weird being able to see her from our tent. Molly, Angelina and I shared one tent and Molly's dad and Matt slept in the other. I was so tired I fell asleep almost immediately.

The next day, Jigsaw had managed to wind herself around her tree and was very pleased to see me.

"You are daft!" I scolded her, kissing her on her nose. "Here's another haynet."

"We couldn't wait to get going on our trek, but first we had to groom the ponies, eat breakfast, tidy up the field (we put all the poo in a pile under the hedge) and then tack up and set off.

"See you this evening!" said Molly's dad, hitching up the trailer.

"We were in real unknown country now – a whole day's ride from home.

"I hope Matt knows how to read that map!" Molly hissed at me. I'd been daydreaming, but hoped she was right.

We rode on all day, stopping every hour or so for a brief rest, a drink and a snack. We found a clear stream where the ponies drank their fill, and Puffin blew water all over Angelina's jodhpurs, giving her a soaking and making her shriek so that Star freaked out and almost pulled the reins out of Molly's hand. Thank goodness she held on – can you imagine what Connie would say if Star had galloped for home?

It was about three thirty when Molly asked Matt how far we were from the next camp site. Matt consulted the map, letting CP munch grass while he looked at it this way and that, turning it upside down and squinting ahead.

"You don't know the way, do you?" asked Angelina, narrowing her eyes acusingly.

"Yes I do, stop worrying!" said Matt, peering again at the map.

"You'd better!" said Molly, darkly.

"Oh yes, or else what?" asked Matt. "If you think you can do a better job, feel free!"

"You do know the way, don't you?" I asked. My bum hurt a bit. Spending all day in the saddle isn't quite the joy I thought it would be. I hoped Jiggy's back didn't hurt her.

"This way!" announced Matt, heading CP off in another direction.

Ten minutes later we arrived at a farm and could see Molly's dad waving at us from the trailer. Phew!

"Had you all going there for a while, didn't I?" said Matt, grinning.

"Ha, ha, not!" scowled Molly.

With the ponies settled we all enjoyed another supper of sausage, burgers and buns. It seemed Molly's dad is no Jamie Oliver – not that we were complaining. We were all starving!

Then we sat around the fire and Matt said he'd tell us a ghost story. It turned out to be a really scary one all about a girl who was haunted by a ghostly presence. He told it with lots of sound effects, and kept shining a torch under his chin, which made him look mad, and then lowered his voice to a whisper while he told us how the girl had dropped a valuable ring in the forest, and had to ride out to find it. Of course, the ghostly presence was there, menacingly, and we all sat wide-eyed with terror as he told us how the girl could hear footsteps behind her, and her pony threw her off and galloped home.

I gulped. I wished we'd never started this and I looked at Molly's dad, hoping he'd stop Matt. But he was loving it, so that was never going to happen.

"And then, the girl could feel the hot breath of the ghostly presence on her neck behind her, and an eerie sound of wailing broke the silence as the girl looked around. And she saw..., she saw..."

Suddenly, there was a deathly shriek and we all jumped about a metre into the air. Angelina clutched at her heart and Molly looked terrified.

"Oh no, Puffin's got loose!" Angelina yelled, jumping to her feet

and dashing off to catch him. He had sidled up to Jiggy and tried to pinch some hay from her net, and she had told him off. Talk about brilliant timing!

A few minutes later, with Puffin safely secured and Jiggy's dignity restored we all sat back down and waited for Matt to finish his story.

"So what happened?" I asked Matt, gulping.

"What was the ghostly presence?" Molly asked.

"Dunno!" said Matt, shrugging his shoulders. I was just making it up as I went along and I've lost interest now. Someone else have a go."

"Oh Matt!" we all screamed, throwing stuff at him. We decided we'd had enough of ghost stories, so we went and said goodnight to the ponies, instead.

"Last day tomorrow!" said Angelina, giving Puffin a cuddle. "Puffin's so cute, I shall hate giving him back after the school hols are over. He's really enjoyed riding out with you guys. It's so lovely spending all day and night with a pony, isn't it?"

"I just have to find the way home," said Matt, winking at me as he fed CP a spare burger bun.

We all set off late in the morning. As everyone was so tired we all overslept – and then Molly's dad burnt breakfast and had to start all over again.

"I never thought I'd say this," Matt told me confidently, as we munched on sausage sandwiches, "but I don't much care if I never see another sausage again!"

We rode though some lovely pine forests, and then the countryside started to look familiar – we were on our way home! The ponies knew it and walked with a spring in their step, but we were all a bit sorry our adventure was over. I know it wasn't much of an adventure – we hadn't rescued anyone, or found buried treasure – but it had been fun all the same.

"We'll have to do this again next holidays," I said, and everyone agreed. Well, the humans agreed – I don't know whether the ponies would be up for it. I asked Jiggy but she just nuzzled my shoulder and blew on my hair. I'm not sure if that means yes or no!

> *We all sat wide-eyed with terror as he told us how the girl could hear footsteps behind her*

THE ANSWERS

How did you do in all our quizzes? Find out here!

M	Y	D	N	U	L	J	R	I	P	O	T	T	O	K	S	U	D	P	J	R	T	I	M	P	R
A	A	R	P	R	B	P	O	N	E	A	H	N	M	G	N	I	N	I	E	R	N	E	D	O	B
R	S	V	W	L	M	U	L	E	E	N	I	M	Y	J	V	W	L	S	L	A	R	O	N	L	C
E	H	H	B	A	O	U	H	D	I	S	E	M	A	G	D	E	T	N	U	O	M	I	I	O	H
M	O	M	O	W	L	C	F	V	T	L	M	A	R	W	A	R	I	N	S	K	U	B	L	M	I
A	W	H	F	W	L	H	M	F	N	C	S	A	I	B	S	P	S	H	E	M	I	A	C	S	N
M	I	W	A	C	J	E	U	N	I	Y	T	J	U	M	P	C	R	O	S	S	E	R	Y	T	C
M	N	R	I	V	A	U	L	T	I	N	G	S	S	O	K	H	P	I	H	D	N	R	G	R	O
O	G	A	C	A	L	O	M	A	S	C	E	E	B	R	I	C	A	M	H	R	N	E	N	E	T
T	C	M	W	H	S	N	L	P	Z	Y	I	S	T	L	R	G	U	N	A	L	Y	L	I	B	E
H	A	H	E	E	D	R	F	M	I	E	N	E	P	O	T	N	K	K	R	F	M	R	S	O	A
J	I	Y	C	N	I	M	A	L	I	N	T	I	S	V	E	I	A	I	M	A	L	A	A	R	G
A	V	B	A	L	I	C	E	N	O	C	G	P	S	S	G	V	T	C	L	N	E	C	H	R	U
C	H	R	O	M	O	S	O	M	E	R	L	U	O	N	S	I	H	P	J	R	I	I	C	F	E
E	N	D	U	R	A	N	C	E	K	A	L	C	M	A	E	R	I	S	K	A	Y	N	E	H	N
Y	J	D	W	L	E	L	A	R	L	I	M	Y	J	V	D	A	S	L	A	O	G	L	I	M
J	E	N	F	A	D	T	H	D	L	E	G	O	J	E	N	B	W	A	T	N	D	I	P	I	T
E	Q	M	F	J	E	S	U	A	T	R	E	L	N	Q	M	F	A	N	I	U	V	T	E	M	N
K	B	H	P	S	O	F	B	T	E	N	T	P	E	G	G	I	N	G	F	C	U	L	E	S	A
E	I	W	A	C	N	E	U	K	E	A	C	S	S	N	W	A	I	T	I	R	K	E	T	T	B
T	I	F	H	Z	S	R	D	R	E	S	S	A	G	E	G	Y	G	X	I	M	O	P	S	R	A
L	S	I	C	R	L	H	R	A	S	C	E	E	B	I	I	C	A	L	H	O	A	S	C	E	R
A	C	U	O	S	N	A	L	N	Z	Y	B	D	X	P	U	W	H	N	A	L	N	Z	Y	B	B
H	A	H	E	R	D	R	F	M	C	E	V	E	N	T	I	N	G	D	R	L	M	C	E	O	E
L	O	R	R	A	I	N	E	T	R	A	V	I	S	A	T	I	N	I	M	O	L	I	G	R	I
A	U	G	S	O	T	R	E	C	A	C	R	P	S	E	S	S	O	R	C	O	L	O	P	N	Z

WHAT ARE THEY DOING PAGES 28–29

1. Dressage 2. Barrel Racing
3. Endurance. 4. Horseball.
5. JumpCross 6. Tent pegging
7. Polo 8. Scurry Driving
9. Stunt riding 10. Show
jumping 11. Polocrosse
12. Vaulting (practice!).

PUZZLE PAGE PAGES 34–35

Odd one out

1. Morgan is the odd one out. The rest are all names for donkeys or mules.
2. Snaffle is the odd one out – the rest are all parts of a saddle.
3. A Shire is a horse – the rest are ponies.
4. Charlotte Dujardin is the only dressage rider in a field of eventers!
5. An Appaloosa is spotty – the rest are broken-coloured.
6. The Haflinger comes from Austria, the rest from the USA.
7. Winvers is made up amongst lateral dressage movements.
8. They're all boots – apart from Knocking, which is made up.
9. Clinker is not a jump – the rest are.
10. All the horses, except Golden Flame, have appeared on TV or in films!

TRAVEL TRAUMA PAGES 50–51

1. A and C are both correct. B is not correct because the trailer should have been mucked out directly after it was last used and left clean and tidy.

2. C is the correct answer. Your pony should be dressed in protective clothing to ensure he does not step on himself or injure himself when travelling. A lightweight rug may be better if it is hot, as the pony might sweat.

3. This tail bandage has been put on badly, and the top of the dock is unprotected. If the pony sits on his tail in transit (which a lot of ponies do!), the tail could be rubbed raw.

4. Here are the wrong things!
1. The handler is wearing

neither hat, nor gloves.
2. The handler is looking at the pony, which will not encourage him to follow her.
3. The handler has not set the pony up to approach the ramp in a straight line, discouraging him to enter.
4. The trailer is dirty, and has no bedding.
5. The pony is wearing brushing boots, not protective travel boots.
6. The pony has no poll protection.
7. The pony is wearing a headcollar – a bridle over the top would give the handler more control.

5. C is the correct way to approach a ramp. The others are all wrong, and will not encourage a pony to load.

6. The correct answer is A.

7. The correct answer is B.

8. The correct answer is B.

WHERE IN THE WORLD? PAGES 62-63

Akhal-Teke = **Turkmenistan**
Andalusian = **Southern Spain**
Appaloosa = **USA (Washington state)**
Arab = **Arabian peninsular**
Ardennais = **French/Belgian border**
Boer = **South Africa**
Connemara = **Ireland**
Falabella = **Argentina**
Fjord = **Norway**
Friesian = **Netherlands**
Haflinger = **Austria**
Morgan = **USA (New England state)**
Orlov trotter= **Russia**
Waler = **Australia**

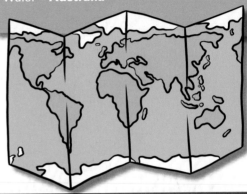

RIDING CHALLENGE PAGES 72–73

The aids (1)
The voice, seat, hands and legs are all natural aids.
The whip and spurs are both artificial aids.

The aids (2)
1. You are asking for canter
2. You are asking for halt
3. You are asking for a turn or circle to the left

Inside... outside...
1. The inside leg asks for impulsion and bend
2. The outside leg influences the pony's quarters
3. The inside hand asks for direction
4. The outside hand controls and regulates the pace and controls the bend.

Pace yourself
There are four beats to the stride in walk and gallop
There are two beats to the stride in trot
There are three beats to the stride in canter

Energy is another word for impulsion

Extended walk, collected walk, working trot, medium canter, extended canter and counter canter are all real paces.
Counter trot and short trot are not real paces.

Diagonal dilemma!
1. True
2. False
3. True

Getting fancy!
The movement described is a turn on the forehand.

Statements 1, 2 and 4 all correctly describe lateral movements.

Unloading safely

WHO'S THE CELEB PAGES 88–89

How did you get on? Some were easy, others not so much! Read on to put you out of your misery!

Who's doing that?
1. Mark Todd 2. Robert Smith 3. Carl Hester 4. Piggy French 5. Ellen Whitaker 6. Pippa Funnell 7. Harry Meade 8. Oliver Townend 9. Lee Pearson 10. Charlotte Dujardin 11. Zara Phillips (tricky – she's very young!).

Doggone it!
A. Laura Collett B. Jessica Mendoza C. Mary King D. Carl Hester E. Tim Stockdale F. Amy Stovold.

Teacher, teacher
1. Oliver Townend. 2. William Funnell 3. Tim Stockdale 4. Lucinda Fredericks 5. Ben Maher 6. William Fox-Pitt 7. Sharon Hunt 8. Carl Hester.

Riders at Home
A. Ben Maher B. Tim Stockdale C. Mark Todd D. Carl Hester E. Lucinda Fredericks F. Pippa Funnell.

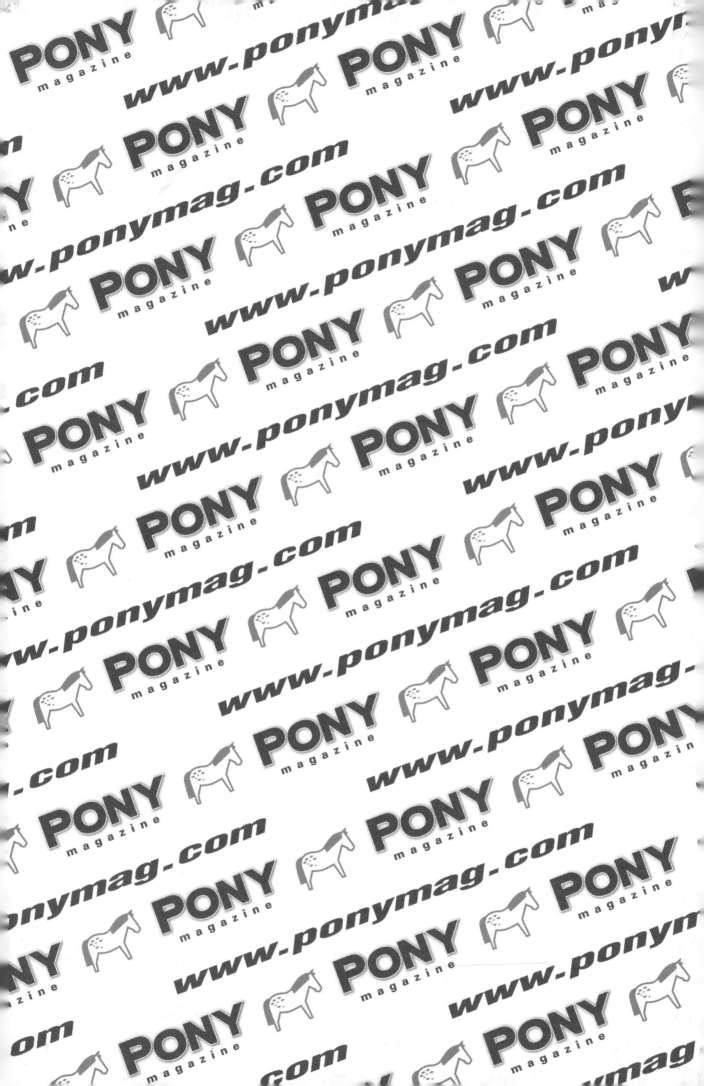